BOOK 1

Edited and introduced by
Richard Browne

TIMES BOOKS

This edition published 2010
First published in 2001 by Times Books as
The Times 2 Crossword Book 1

HarperCollins*Publishers*
77–85 Fulham Palace Road
Hammersmith
London W6 8JB

www.collins.co.uk

1

ISBN 9780007885763

A catalogue record for this book is available from the British Library.

Typeset in Great Britain by
Davidson Pre-Press Graphics Ltd, Glasgow G3

Printed and bound in Great Britain by
Clays Ltd, Suffolk

INTRODUCTION

These puzzles, which appeared in *The Times* during 1997, are clued with definitions only, but they are not too easy. They should appeal to the typical *Times* reader, as they assume a reasonably wide vocabulary and an acquaintance with at least the principal peaks of our historical and cultural heritage. Recourse to reference books should not be needed.

Some of the puzzles have a little extra in them, if you care to look for it – it is never essential to solving the puzzle. Some themes are obvious, such as the running quotation in no. 71 (the Christmas Eve puzzle). Some puzzles have a group of related answers, such as nos. 23 and 63; others, something visible in the completed grid, as with no. 37. It may also help to know that puzzle no. 1 appeared originally as *Times 2* no. 1000, and no. 11 as no. 1066. I will leave you to look for the theme of no. 74 (hint: 1 across), and to spot why no. 20 was scheduled for February 14th. (Answers below.)

(Answers: No. 20 – read the letters in the diagonal from top left to bottom right. No. 74 – three bear names among the answers, and the word BEAR hidden three times in the grid.)

Richard Browne
Times 2 Editor

THE PUZZLES

ACROSS

1 Make accessible; speak more freely (4,2)

5 Refund of excess (6)

8 Give meal to (4)

9 Remember its Fifth (8)

10 Level, polished (6)

12 French clerical title, e.g. Liszt's (4)

15 Points, levels of being less good (13)

16 Labyrinth (4)

17 Money of Portugal (6)

19 Capital of Chile (8)

21 Greet; falling stones (4)

22 Ship; liquid holder (6)

23 Caught sight of (6)

DOWN

2 Inflamed-lung illness (9)

3 Show agreement; Cain's land (3)

4 Bat in emergency (*baseball*) (5-3)

5 Wander (4)

6 Pompously high-flown (in speech) (9)

7 Digit; sounds like *haul* (3)

11 Egg dishes (9)

13 Subsistence level (9)

14 Inspiring horror, disgust (8)

18 Missionary apostle; — Jones, dance (4)

20 Champion; point-winning serve (3)

21 Jump; beer ingredient (3)

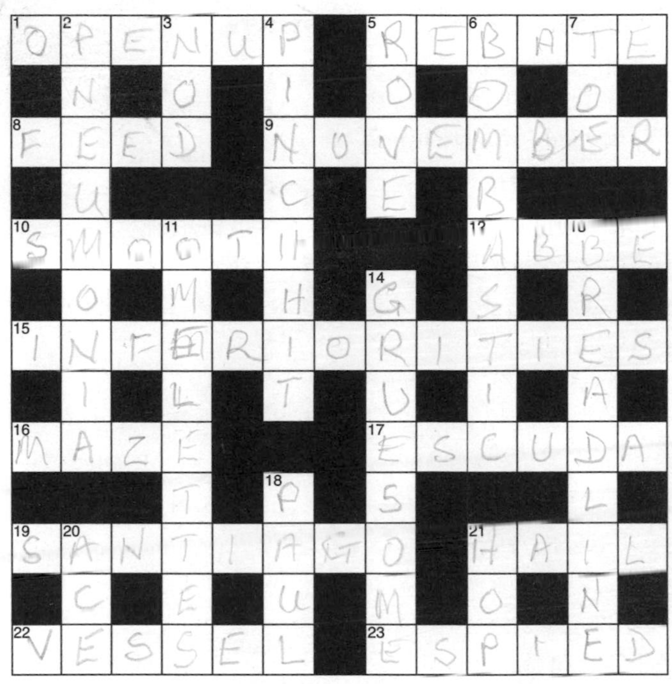

ACROSS

1 Self-controlled (after Greek philosophers) (5)

7 Charged (with crime) (7)

8 Deep red shade (7)

9 Smokers' saucer (7)

11 Draw out (6)

13 K, Q, or J (5,4)

15 Friction-reducing substance (9)

19 Of the French (6)

21 Sleep (*colloq.*) (4-3)

23 Trace; tiny remnant (7)

24 Bravery (7)

25 Animal track (5)

DOWN

1, 20 Paris basilica (5,5)

2 Source (6)

3 Of the universe (6)

4 Water-into-wine miracle town (4)

5 Of the countryside (6)

6 Restoration work; goes (7)

10 Twine (6)

12 Sensitive to slights (6)

14 Snooker-table edge (7)

16 Lab vessel; sharp reply (6)

17 Heel/ankle bones (6)

18 Creature with missing pigment (6)

20 See 1 *dn*

22 Level (4)

ACROSS

1 Daffodils (8)

5 Capital of Norway (4)

8 Filthy look; overbrightness (5)

9 (Rocket) start to rise (4,3)

11 Tiny –, *Christmas Carol* cripple (3)

12 Riddle (9)

13 Join the forces (6)

15 Creeks of the sea (6)

18 Health, vitality (4-5)

19 Poor –, Edgar's disguise (*Lear*) (3)

20 Localised speech (7)

21 Wall-painting (5)

22 Get clean (4)

23 Uneven (contest) (3-5)

DOWN

1 Woman's bedwear (7)

2 Kingdom (5)

3 Not to be forgiven (11)

4 Unspeaking (6)

6 Whip; one harassing (7)

7 Foreign-aid charity (5)

10 Exciting activity (3,3,5)

14 Burns's Scottish 20 (7)

16 Tasted; took specimens (7)

17 Pay attention (6)

18 Victoria, *the – at Windsor* (*Kipling*) (5)

19 Weary (5)

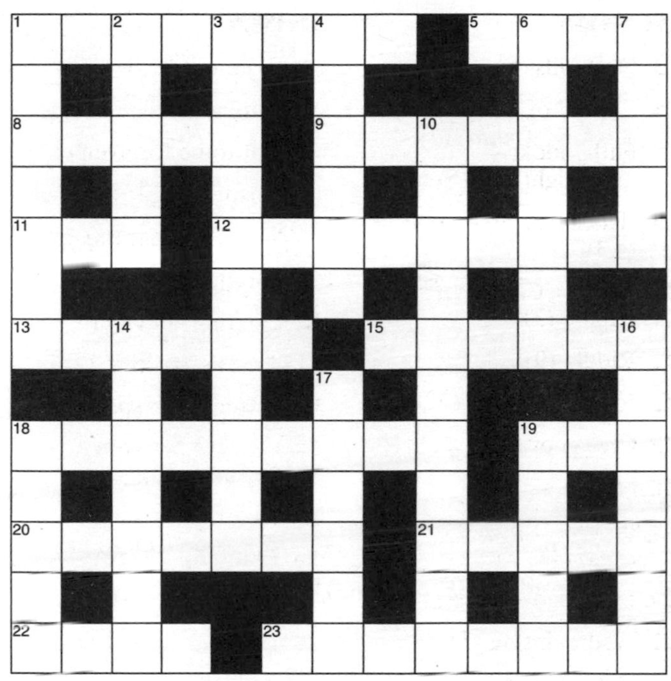

ACROSS

1 Place of light confinement (4,6)

8 Dissolve (team) (7)

9 Greek *A* (5)

10 Make tea, beer (4)

11 Useless item; failure (4,4)

13 Water behind reef (6)

15 Unconscious (6)

17 Feeling gratitude (8)

18 Piece of money (4)

21 Social grouping (5)

22 Property theft (7)

23 Aggrieved, bitter feelings (10)

DOWN

2 Ski course (5)

3 Minimum type of tide (4)

4 Africa/Arabia divider (3,3)

5 Carelessly quick (8)

6 Roman god of 19 (7)

7 Naughty, dishonest behaviour (5-5)

8 Make feeble (10)

12 (Given) permanently (3,5)

14 River of ice (7)

16 Exhibiting 23 (6)

19 Large body of water (5)

20 Looking stern, harsh (4)

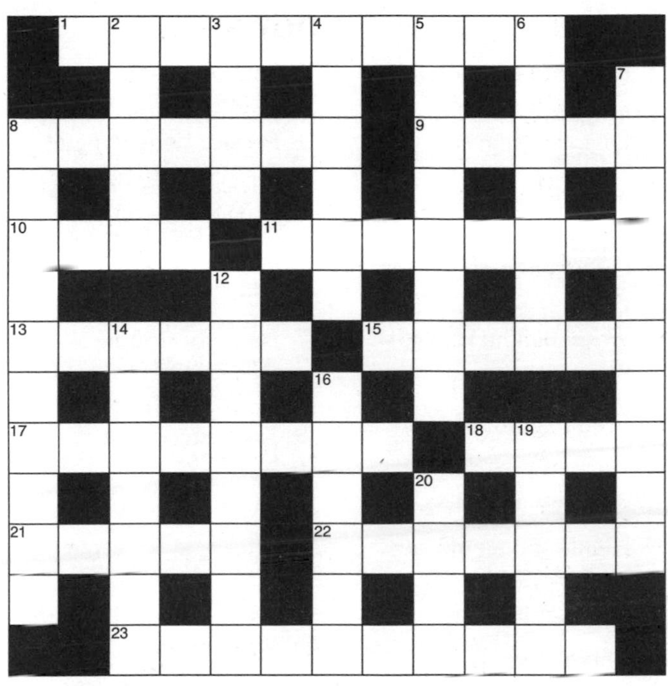

ACROSS

1 Newborn to pride (4,3)

5 Mutilate (4)

9 Burdened (5)

10 Two-line verse (7)

11 Impossible to stomach (12)

12 Language group including Gaelic, Welsh (6)

13 *Last Theorem* mathematician (6)

16 Have to retract (statement) (3,4,5)

19 Highly influential; able to develop (7)

20 Jewelled headdress (5)

21 Completed (4)

22 Park wardens (7)

DOWN

1 Temporarily inactive period (4)

2 Service book; type of number (7)

3 Teaching to respond to stimulus (12)

4 Pail (6)

6 Off-the-cuff (2-3)

7 Annual car check-up (3,4)

8 Kick one who is down (3,3,4,2)

12 Needing ironing (7)

14 Intervene to reconcile (7)

15 Block of building stone (6)

17 Athenian misanthrope (*Shakespeare*) (5)

18 Spoils; Roman god (4)

ACROSS

1 Daybreak (4)

3 Israel tribe; Jacob's youngest (8)

8 Cheat of payment (4)

9 Inclination, bent (8)

11 Unpleasantly modern (10)

14 Out of one's mind (6)

15 Predicament; just pass (exam) (6)

17 Prerequisite (4,3,3)

20 (Impractical) perfection seeker (8)

21 Fail to achieve (4)

22 Peripatetic drinking session (3,5)

23 Incline; thin (4)

DOWN

1 Carefree, urbane (8)

2 19th century US frontier zone (4,4)

4 Vigour (6)

5 Racing ruling body (6,4)

6 Sound mournful (4)

7 Observe; brief jotting (4)

10 Analgesic (10)

12 Yellow-skin disease (8)

13 *In Memoriam* poet (8)

16 Up-and-down plaything (3-3)

18 Thin scrap (cloud, material) (4)

19 Plant for flavouring (4)

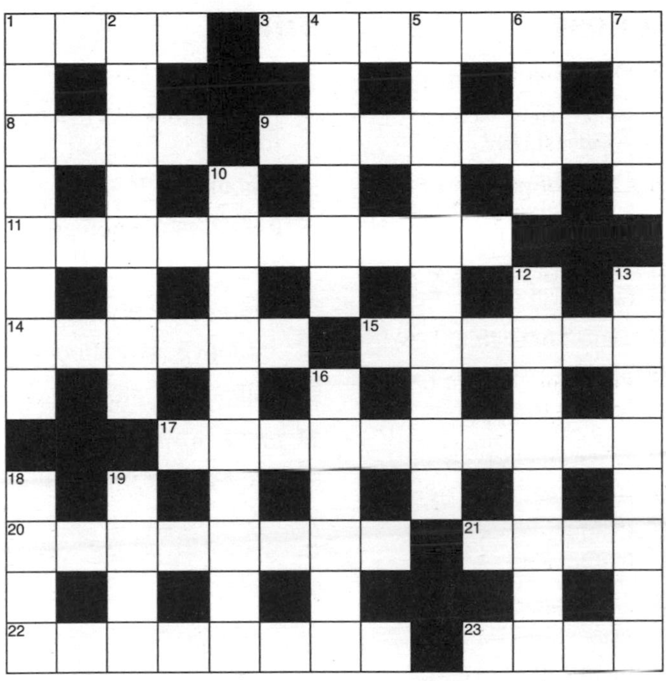
1
2
3
4
5
6
7
8
9
10
11
12
13
14
15
16
17
18
19
20
21
22
23

ACROSS

1 An army; a party-giver (4)

3 Small falcon (7)

8 Prince, chose gold casket (*Merchant of Venice*) (7)

9 E.g. potato root (5)

10 Name (of e.g. book) (5)

11 Engagingly attractive (7)

13 Gangster chief (9)

17 Rips veil off (7)

19 A parable; *worse* (*anagram*) (5)

20 Chinese black/white animal (5)

22 Tribal chief (7)

23 Member of white-rose party (7)

24 Gaming stake (4)

DOWN

1, 15 Egg that sat on a wall (6,6)

2 Ploy (9)

3 Be worldly wise (4,5,4)

4 The Devil (5)

5 Difficulty; polish (3)

6 Pantry (6)

7 Smooth cement floor (6)

12 Lady rower (9)

14 Light cavalryman (6)

15 See 1 *dn*

16 An alloy; an Age; a statue (6)

18 Hindu holy man (5)

21 And not (3)

8

ACROSS

1 Be indecisive (9)
6 Tedious task; cigarette (3)
8 Clever; with a cutting edge (5)
9 Innate; unaffected (7)
10 Curving outwards (6)
12 Show as untrue (5)
13 A tree; neat (6)
14 Parliament clock tower (3,3)
17 Put lid on (5)
19 Immoral; sacrilegious (6)
21 Surround; envelop (7)
22 Divided into areas (5)
23 Agent (3)
24 Sleepy (9)

DOWN

1 Flower receptacle (4)
2 Outcry (7)
3 Part of face; cheek (3)
4 Building extension (6)
5 Found; ascertain (9)
6 Running wild (animal) (5)
7 Spanish treasure ship (7)
11 Done through another (9)
13 Achievement of aim (7)
15 Equilibrium (7)
16 Exhibition building (6)
18 Pétain's capital (5)
20 Having lost fizz (4)
22 Animal exhibition (3)

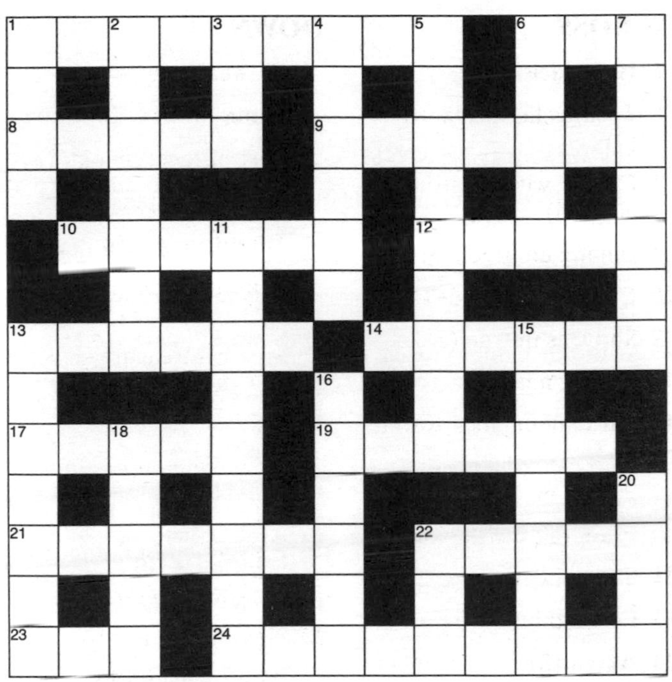

ACROSS

1 Hobby (7)

5 Boring; cloudy (4)

8 Silk strip for tying, etc. (6)

9 Filthy (stables Hercules cleaned) (6)

10 Sheath for sword (8)

12 Portent (4)

13 With which not to touch the hated (9)

17 Huge (4)

18 Posh dance hall (8)

20 Spasmodic, intermittent (6)

21 Consternation (6)

23 Earth; to make dirty (4)

24 Navigation instrument (7)

DOWN

2 For each person (6)

3 Vessel; Swift's *Tale* of one (3)

4 Miraculous food; unexpected gift (5)

5 Priest's neckwear (3,6)

6 One taking charge (6)

7 Short of money (4,2)

11 Delighting the eye (9)

14 Eat fast; make turkey noise (6)

15 Gambling house (6)

16 Area of land, of knowledge (6)

19 House at drive entrance (5)

22 Relax; take (exam) (3)

ACROSS

1 Good-luck charm (6)

5 Seize (4)

9 Where Don John of Austria beat Turks (*Chesterton*) (7)

10 Reason for action (6)

11 Light-hearted repartee (8)

12 Servants' uniform (6)

15 It is *a lovesome thing, God wot* (*T. E. Brown*) (6)

18 Sheriff's officer (8)

20 Unrivalled (6)

22 Orgy of destruction (7)

23 Entrance; number attending match (4)

24 Speckled hen; a county (6)

DOWN

2 Muslim scholar (6)

3 Unbalanced (8)

4 Indian two-wheeler; Friendly Islands (5)

6 Humiliating defeat (4)

7 Dam-building rodent (6)

8 Unpretentious; (US) ugly (girl) (6)

13 Provisions of food (8)

14 Detain (enemy aliens) (6)

16 Canvas shelter (6)

17 Weak; over-refined (6)

19 Presses for information; shoes (5)

21 Abandon; resign (4)

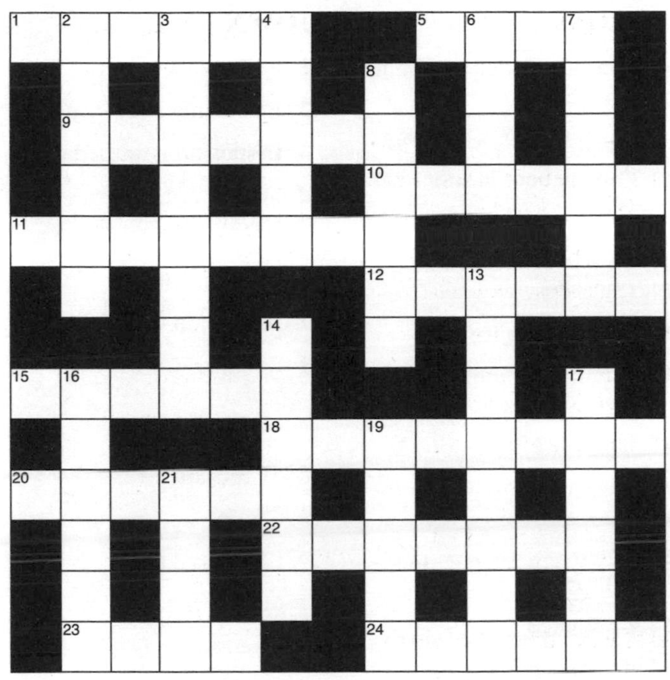

ACROSS

3 Club; protected mammal (3)

8 Road to house; compel (5)

9 One without illusions (7)

10 One without credulity (7)

11 Wood-shaping machine (5)

12 Grass-cutter (6)

14 Breathe painfully; bright idea (6)

15 Esoteric (6)

17 Rival of classical Athens (6)

20 *Manfred, Don Juan* poet (5)

21 Contented (7)

24 Spouse's child, not one's own (7)

25 Calls; feature of Saturn (5)

26 Element Sn (3)

DOWN

1 Probability (4)

2 Best clothes (6)

3 Disposition; warped (4)

4 Stretch of land (5)

5 High-masted vessel (4,4)

6 Not much (6)

7 And so on (2,6)

12 Looking down on "inferiors" (8)

13 Sanctity (8)

16 Membrane over eye (6)

18 Getting up; revolt (6)

19 Exhausted (5)

22 Make (money) (4)

23 Sleep rough (4)

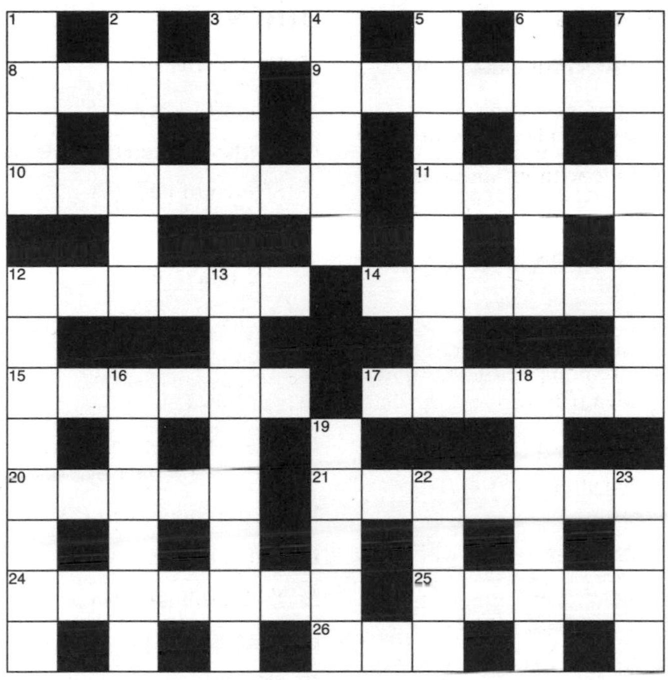

12

ACROSS

1 Free from blame (7)

5 Rugby formation (5)

8 Cavalry unit (5)

9 Claude —, French composer (7)

10 Silent; act in mime (3)

11 Dancer's twirl (9)

12 Suicide bird (*Mikado*) (3-3)

14 Magician (6)

17 Birnam Wood came to it (*Macbeth*) (9)

18 Fasten; (golf) hole marker (3)

19 Insufficient attention (7)

20 Sphere (5)

21 Swell; sudden increase (5)

22 Muslim fast (7)

DOWN

1 Endeavour (7)

2 Great fuss, wind (5)

3 Drink with tongue; circuit (3)

4 Tolerate (6)

5 Not for discussion outside court (3,6)

6 Egypt town, hieroglyph-key stone (7)

7 Perhaps (5)

11 Special benefit, immunity (9)

13 Department head (7)

15 Deep, dismal cell (7)

16 Divisor; business agent (6)

17 Sand hills (5)

18 Sticking out; arrogant (5)

20 Type of tree; part of mouth (3)

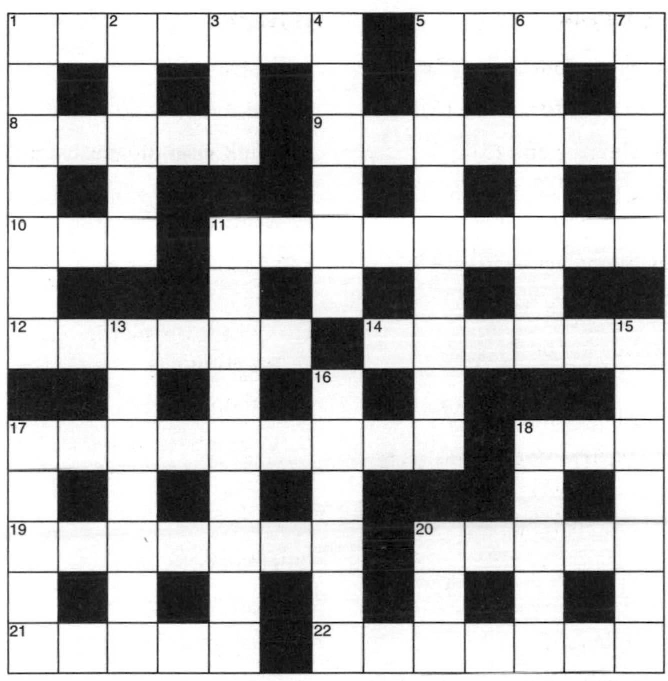

ACROSS

1 War/disaster relief agency (3,5)

5 Part of hand; trophy (4)

9 Be all one deserves (5,3,5)

10 Stabiliser; sounds like *benefit cheque* (4)

11 Hazardous polar mass, may calve (7)

13 Rudderless (6)

15 Old and useless (4,2)

18 Holder of responsible post (7)

20 Two of Henry VIII's wives (4)

23 Trouble in store (especially for Faust) (3,5,2,3)

24 Be excessively fond (4)

25 Falstaff's red-nosed crony (8)

DOWN

1 Iron rot (4)

2 Unclean (5)

3 Recite rapidly, easily (4,3)

4 Penalty box (hockey) (3,3)

6 To increase (7)

7 Lessen severity of (8)

8 Unconfined (4)

12 Strangled by wire (8)

14 Think; bounce back (7)

16 Modified (7)

17 Three-horse Russian vehicle (6)

19 Head cook (4)

21 Gurkha homeland (5)

22 Popular but false idea (4)

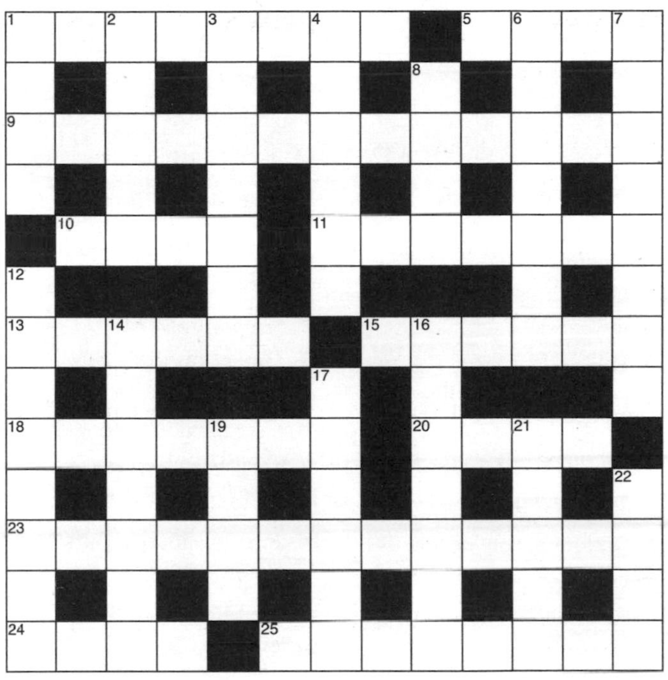

ACROSS

1 Tiny bit (of learning) (10)

8 Siegfried —, war poet (7)

9 Deeper; ring on target (5)

10 Well-ventilated (4)

11 How the unprepared are caught (2,3,3)

13 John —; — Beardsley (6)

15 Indelible skin picture (6)

17 Ceremonious Catholic service (4,4)

18 Amongst (4)

21 A small whale (5)

22 Diplomat; sort of case (7)

23 Methodical (10)

DOWN

2 Tightwad (5)

3 Stepped; "generations have —" (*Hopkins*) (4)

4 Pacific warming current (2,4)

5 One from Emerald Isle (8)

6 Firing of bullet (7)

7 Barset bishop's wife (*Trollope*) (3,7)

8 One disliking going out (4-2-4)

12 With no visible join (8)

14 Past misdemeanours (forgiven) (7)

16 Condition; lands (6)

19 Speed of sound (4,1)

20 Sicilian volcano (4)

ACROSS

1 Relief road (6)

4 Hateful (6)

9 Prefect; type of lizard (7)

10 Take tiny steps; grind up (5)

11 Covered in creeper (5)

13 Most large (7)

14 A long way (3)

15 Item, object (5)

16 Barley drink (3)

17 Brother, sister (7)

19 Cereal fungus (5)

21 Very fat (5)

22 Put to use; asked (for job) (7)

24 Nakedness (6)

25 Collect together (6)

DOWN

1 Cute animated deer (5)

2 Bike basket (7)

3 (Parliament) was in session (3)

5 Inflammatory speaker (9)

6 Small fluid, dry measure (5)

7 Put (sword) away (7)

8 Land of giants *(Gulliver)* (11)

12 Disadvantage (9)

14 Cover (with bunting) (7)

16 Mental agony (7)

18 Mixture (of e.g. flavours) (5)

20 Royal house of Elizabeth I (5)

23 Ball in whistle (3)

ACROSS

3 Animal with trunk (8)

7 Battle of Hastings tapestry (6)

8 Painful; a beer (6)

9 Nun's headdress (6)

10 Prestige; official seal once (6)

11 Counterfeit (4)

13 Just about manage (3,2)

15 Old Testament book after Hosea (4)

17 Bill of exchange; sounds like *verify* (6)

18 Frightened (6)

19 Lebanon capital (6)

20 Take up again (6)

21 *Hamlet* setting, castle (8)

DOWN

1 Yacht harbour (6)

2 Place of worship; part of head (6)

3 Cost (7)

4 Absence of intrusion (7)

5 Unappealing principal character (8)

6 Prepare to flee (4,4)

11 Violent (8)

12 Dynamics (8)

13 Tahiti painter (7)

14 Amusingly curious (7)

15 A legal expert (6)

16 Mystery (6)

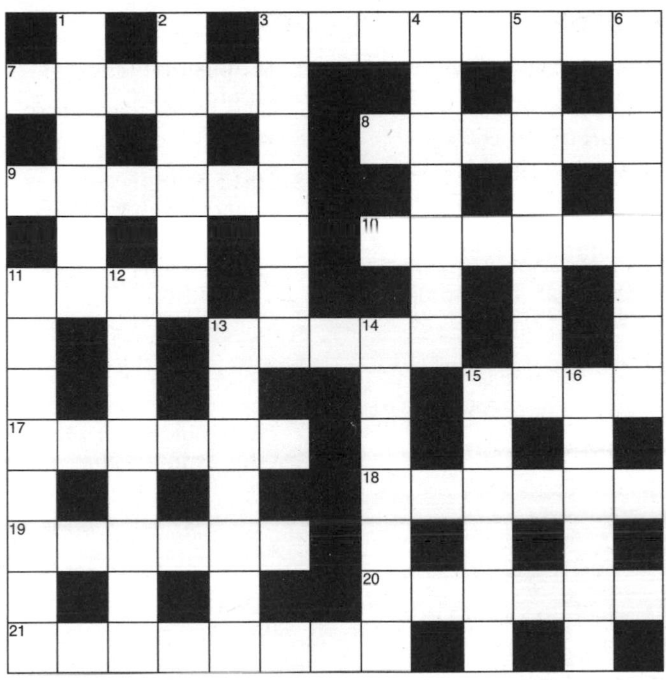

ACROSS

1 Entry recording sum owed (5)

4 Part of Greece; ideal rural country (7)

8 The Waltz King (7)

9 Climb up (5)

10 Be mean with; spell (of work) (5)

11 Annual dog show (6)

13 Strongly encourage (6)

15 Insipid; dry (6)

18 Sick feeling (6)

20 Damaged; penniless (5)

22 (Illicit) love affair (5)

23 The boss (*slang*) (3,4)

24 Be forced back (7)

25 Excavated; seeded with bombs (5)

DOWN

1 Serious misfortune, failure (8)

2 Polish (7)

3 Have confidence in; financial vehicle (5)

4 North-east France region, by Rhine (6)

5 Calculate (7)

6 Intimidate (by difficulty) (5)

7 High male voice (4)

12 Allowed to go free (8)

14 Shyness; spare supply (7)

16 Ideal but impractical (7)

17 Small (often scented) bag (6)

19 Up (e.g. in rigging) (5)

20 Twig broom (5)

21 Just; middling (4)

ACROSS

1 Cut short (9)

6 Group of tennis games (3)

8 Authoritatively approve (7)

9 Florida resort (5)

10 "O! for a Muse of –" (*Henry the 17 dn*) (4)

11 Flag; normal (8)

13 Hired assassin (*slang*) (3,3)

14 Robber outlaw (6)

17 Free-form music; Disney 18 *ac* (8)

18 Thin coating layer (4)

20 Hurries; takes a plane (5)

21 Thin flow (7)

22 Ugly old witch (3)

23 Concurrence; 2 *dn* (9)

DOWN

1 See 4 *dn* (7)

2 Intelligence; sympathy (13)

3 Brusquely brief (4)

4 "Come kiss me, sweet and –" (*1 dn Night*) (6)

5 Fiendishly inspired, frantic (8)

6 Amorous activity (4,3,6)

7 See 16 *dn* (5)

12 Asian federation (8)

15 See 19 *dn* (7)

16 "The – of our discontent" (*Richard the 7 dn*) (6)

17 See 10 *ac* (5)

19 "Full fathom –" (*The 15 dn*) (4)

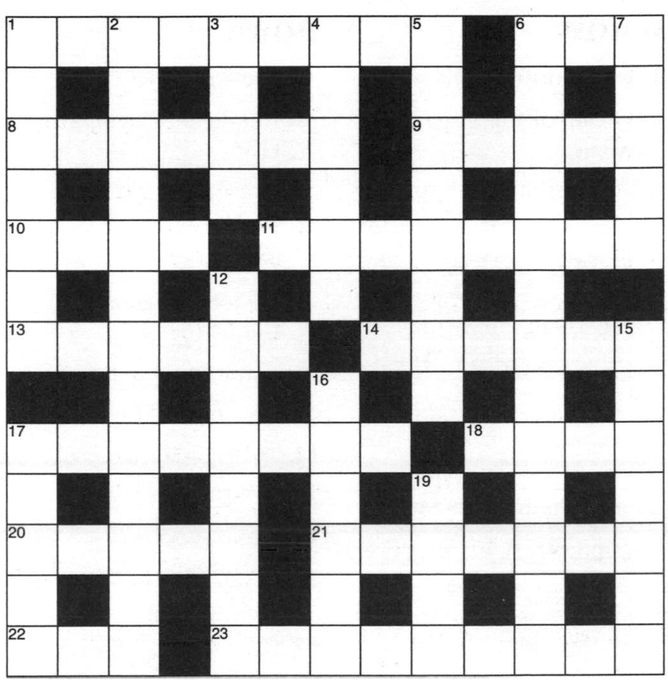

ACROSS

1 *Tempest* magician (8)

7 Listlessness (5)

8 Width between surfaces (9)

9 Expression of disgust (3)

10 Head growth (4)

11 Forcibly apply (6)

13 Hat; car engine cover (6)

14 Having talent (6)

17 Distinct smell; enjoy this (6)

18 Small mountain (4)

20 Capture; cricket practice (3)

22 One successful with women (6,3)

23 Fine, attractive; (especially baby) healthy (5)

24 (Excuse) cease to convince (4,4)

DOWN

1 Small piece, plot (5)

2 Point of view (7)

3 Fish; weapon; (Northern) 18 (4)

4 French coronation city (6)

5 Excessive (5)

6 Seen; able to see (7)

7 Ex-Soviet republic, capital Tallinn (7)

12 With weight (7)

13 Eventually (2,3,2)

15 Great success (7)

16 "Come follow the 13 *ac* of 23 —" (*Scott*) (6)

17 Unfeeling; hard (5)

19 Underclothing (5)

21 Look closely (4)

20

ACROSS

4 Long-life (milk) (1,1,1)

8 Made of baked clay (7)

9 Fight off (attacker) (5)

10 Stratum; a hen (5)

11 Yield easily to (desire) (7)

12 In shy, humble way (8)

14 Floating platform (4)

15 Appearance (4)

16 Naive; several Popes (8)

20 Commit, deliver (7)

21 Method of employment (5)

23 Simple dress; an expedient (5)

24 Bizarre, Dali-esque (7)

25 Word of assent (3)

DOWN

1 Calf-skin parchment (6)

2 A Paris airport (4)

3 Prickles (6)

4 Reluctance (13)

5 Exchange of goods (5)

6 A slopping (of liquid) (8)

7 Flowing, speaking, easily (6)

13 Spike; *as dead as* it (8)

15 Plague grasshopper (6)

17 Collected works (6)

18 By three times (6)

19 Walter –, Thurber's fantasist (5)

22 Yemen port, once British (4)

ACROSS

2 Pale yellow-green (3-2-3)

6 Negligent (6)

8 Sacred river; actress/mistress of William IV (6)

9 Contradict (7)

10 Trail dogs follow (5)

12 Seductive (glance) (4-6)

16 Wall anti-moisture layer (4,6)

18 Issue a share (5)

20 Simon –, South American liberator (7)

21 Remove cover (from face, plaque) (6)

22 Corset; sort of scone/cake (6)

23 Go beyond; welfare activism (8)

DOWN

1 Six-sided figure (7)

2 A retreat into fantasy (8)

3 Be half-asleep (6)

4 Poke gently (5)

5 Distance along (6)

7 Sly suggestion (8)

11 Gaming table officiant (8)

13 Diaphragm spasm (8)

14 Attack (7)

15 Enrico –, tenor (died 1921) (6)

17 (Fine) clothes (6)

19 Greenish woollen mixture (5)

ACROSS

1 Macintosh (8)

5 E.g. top-of-pond film (4)

9 Government press-censoring request (1-6)

10 – Keller; – of Troy (5)

11 – Blyton (4)

12 EU food-additive identifier (1,6)

14 New driver's sign (1-5)

16 Part of oyster season (1,5)

19 Batsman's turn (7)

21 June 6, 1944 (1-3)

24 Both (*arch.*); Mark –, author (5)

25 Disease (7)

26 Red gem (4)

27 In adhesive fashion (8)

DOWN

1 Insulting; unpolished (4)

2 New Testament book after II Peter (1,4)

3 Burma resistance fighter (World War 2) (7)

4 Sixth-former's exam (1,5)

6 Son of Sycorax (*Tempest*) (7)

7 State with king (8)

8 You (*arch.*) (4)

13 Monastic walk (8)

15 Script Ventris deciphered (6,1)

17 Note between staves (piano score) (6,1)

18 Informal top (1-5)

20 Socially naff (3-1)

22 One from Baku (5)

23 Child's guessing game (1,3)

ACROSS

1 Record; subdue (3,4)

5 Members of scrum (4)

8 Chief conspirator (*Julius Caesar*) (6)

9 Place of bliss (6)

10 Aggressive masculinity (8)

12 Sort of bun, chair, cube (4)

13 Church elder (9)

17 Cheap clearance (4)

18 London station; crushing defeat (8)

20 Forswear (6)

21 Forearm-flexing muscle (6)

23 Hacked out (4)

24 Crusaders' Arab opponent (7)

DOWN

2 Imaginary (6)

3 Speck; Morse signal (3)

4 Aristophanes play; insects (5)

5 Improvise (4,2,3)

6 Bring into existence (6)

7 Selective (6)

11 Lover of Columbine (9)

14 Woodcutter; Twain hero (6)

15 Chatter incoherently (6)

16 Hairpiece (6)

19 Small Indian drum-pair (5)

22 US spy bureau (1,1,1)

ACROSS

1 Apparent; feigned (10)

8 Very fortunate (7)

9 Cut of pig; brought home by the successful (5)

10 Watery part of clotting milk (4)

11 Lawyers' jargon (8)

13 Art style, especially of ordinary scenes (5)

14 A daisy plant (2-3)

16 Eruption (e.g. of war, disease) (8)

17 South-east Asia country, capital Vientiane (4)

20 A border river; a cloth (5)

21 Element of army division (7)

22 Shiftless type (4-2-4)

DOWN

1 Lake from horseshoe river bend (5)

2 Immediately (5,3,4)

3 Bouquet (of wine) (4)

4 Certainly (6)

5 Type of dog; part of Canada (8)

6 *1001 Nights* storyteller (12)

7 Violent spasm of 3 (6)

12 Resent (8)

13 An increase (6)

15 Curved surface of road (6)

18 Sense associated with 3 (5)

19 Fodder tower; missile hole (4)

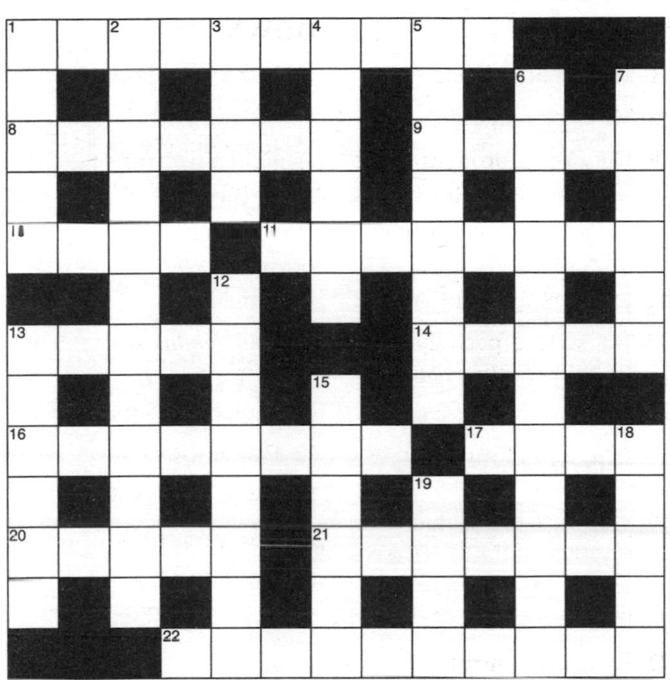

ACROSS

1 From Scandinavia (6)

5 Ready for marriage (6)

8 Very keen, desirous (4)

9 Aggressively active (8)

10 Serious, painful (harm, loss) (8)

12 Hoot; make goose sound (4)

13 Offa's kingdom (6)

15 Reach destination (6)

17 Hideous (4)

19 Tempting, alluring (8)

21 Oil-rich water off Britain (5,3)

23 Fruit; a coveted job (4)

24 Taken by thief (6)

25 Stupid talk (6)

DOWN

2 Head-side of coin (7)

3 Move swiftly to avoid (5)

4 Reach maturity (4,2,3)

5 Nothing (3)

6 Meat trader (7)

7 V. I. Ulyanov pseudonym (5)

11 Plastic money, with microchip (5,4)

14 Cut glass; sort of ball, Palace (7)

16 Risky enterprise (7)

18 Tile mortar (5)

20 Bay of Naples island (5)

22 Err morally (3)

ACROSS

1 Little lab vessel (4,4)
5 Discover (4)
8 Party decorations; swells up (8)
9 Fight; nautical pole (4)
11 Usurping military clique (5)
12 Royal household officer (7)
13 Ploy (6)
15 Inelegant helping (of food) (6)
18 Word of identical meaning (7)
19 More than adequate (5)
21 Ceremony (4)
22 Ingenious contrivance (8)
23 Friendly; close to answer (4)
24 Large celebration (8)

DOWN

1 Man-with-hat-shaped mug (4,3)
2 Beauty parlour; art exhibition room (5)
3 Rich/poor gulf (*Disraeli*) (3,7)
4 Golf hazard; underground shelter (6)
6 Put at risk (7)
7 Elizabeth Bennet's match (*Jane Austen*) (5)
10 Dangerously exposed (3,2,1,4)
14 Enormous; deformed thing (7)
16 Go ahead of (7)
17 Mafia code of secrecy (6)
18 Dry stalks; their colour (5)
20 Before; senior monk (5)

ACROSS

4 Point of fork (5)

7 Twaddle (8)

8 Occur; collapse (4)

9 Glasses without arms (5-3)

10 Loud hooter (6)

13 Engaged man (6)

14 Catcalled (6)

15 Command, requirement (*literary*) (6)

18 Politeness, polite act (8)

19 Space; part of house (4)

20 Discover (technique) again (8)

21 Feudal lord; Belgian city (5)

DOWN

1 Tie up (property); have as consequence (6)

2 Mass arrival (6)

3 Offensive tool (6)

4 Observe (8)

5 Munitions (8)

6 Greedily swallow (e.g. petrol) (6)

11 Sufficient (8)

12 Opera prelude (8)

14 African dog-like scavenger (6)

15 Past; remote places in the back of it (6)

16 Don't stir up its nest (6)

17 Snobbish (*slang*) (6)

ACROSS

5 Place limits round (12)

8 African country; old coin (6)

9 South American blowpipe poison (6)

10 Player on North's left (4)

12 Schematic drawing (7)

14 A mollusc; a sinister power (7)

15 Assert as untrue (4)

17 Fisherman (6)

18 Association; old distance (6)

20 Tricky quibbling (12)

DOWN

1 Passive agreement (12)

2 Grain husks (4)

3 With e.g. telepathic powers (7)

4 Adjourn (parliament) (8)

6 Salt Lake state (4)

7 Gordon Riots novel (*Dickens*) (7,5)

11 Tobias —, 18th century novelist (8)

13 Go rotten (7)

16 Jam up; footwear (4)

19 Similar, related (4)

ACROSS

1 Drug-affected; (game) slightly off (4)

3 Tending to silence (8)

9 Aromatic flavouring (5)

10 Keep; *dialect* (*anagram*) (7)

11 Instance; pattern (7)

12 Gloomy darkness (4)

14 Angular unit, app. 57° (6)

16 Have ambition (6)

18 Dispose of (4)

19 Little thorn (7)

22 Colleague, ally (7)

23 Unaccompanied (5)

24 Drama interval; its music (8)

25 Check and correct (text) (4)

DOWN

1 Pub (8)

2 Tolerate what can't be changed (4,3,4,2)

4 Bowman (6)

5 Narrow neck of land (7)

6 Llaregyb play (*Dylan Thomas*) (5,4,4)

7 River of Sudan, Egypt (4)

8 Agency secretary (4)

13 Deeply respectful (8)

15 Site of 1996 Olympics (7)

17 Soul; mood; alcohol (6)

20 Teheran its capital (4)

21 Church recess (4)

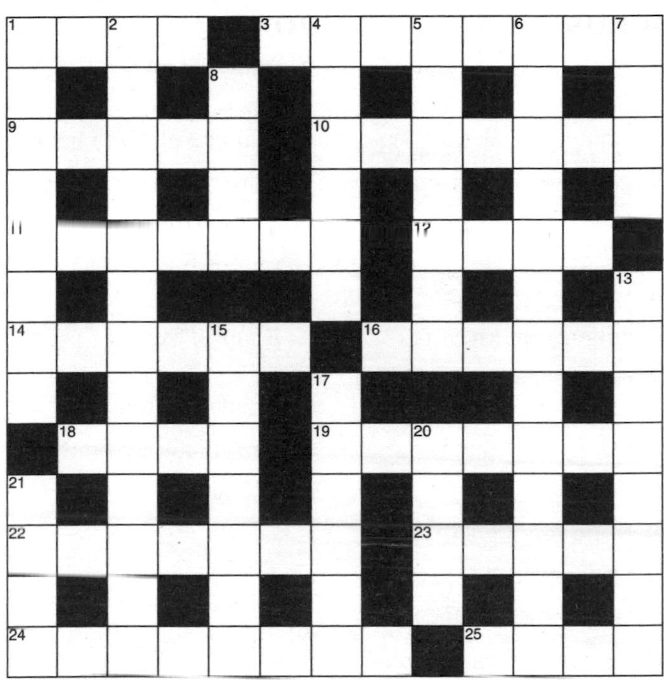

ACROSS

1 Walk through water (4)

3 Played for time (7)

8 Immediate; moment (7)

9 Sequence; command (5)

10 Temptress; aquatic creature (5)

11 Lacking energy, enthusiasm (7)

13 Game; horse-trial site (9)

17 Alas! (*archaic, jocular*) (3,2,2)

19 Assessed (5)

20 Not quite dry (paint) (5)

22 Raging fire (7)

23 Welsh town, castle; *Men of* it (7)

24 Conspiracy; piece of ground (4)

DOWN

1 Caprice; offbeat humour (6)

2 Attractive; worth having (9)

3 TV-reception saucer (9,4)

4 Oak fruit (5)

5 Old money; hallucinogen (*abbr.*) (1,1,1)

6 Mock (6)

7 (Expression) showing distress (6)

12 Artificial (9)

14 List of prices (6)

15 Spasmodic jerk (6)

16 Nimble, quick (6)

18 Distinctive manner (5)

21 Private vehicle (3)

ACROSS

7 Bootleg whiskey (US) (5)

8 Frankness (7)

9 War of the Worlds invader (*Wells*) (7)

10 Compositional idea (5)

11 A mammal; fasten up (4)

12 Intense white lamp (8)

15 Give account of (8)

16 Peruvian Indian (4)

19 Desert waterhole; pop group (5)

21 "Like a — in the sky" (*Carroll*) (3-4)

22 Mounted bullfighter (7)

23 Where Joan of Arc burned (5)

DOWN

1 — Edison, Gainsborough (6)

2 19th century pauper regulations (4,4)

3 Singing group (5)

4 Irregular datum (7)

5 Booty (4)

6 Gain (6)

8 One chipping in (11)

13 Unstinting (8)

14 Study of metre and verse (7)

15 Is limp; sounds like *fruit with stones* (6)

17 Nobody in particular (6)

18 Native New Zealander (5)

20 Footwear item (4)

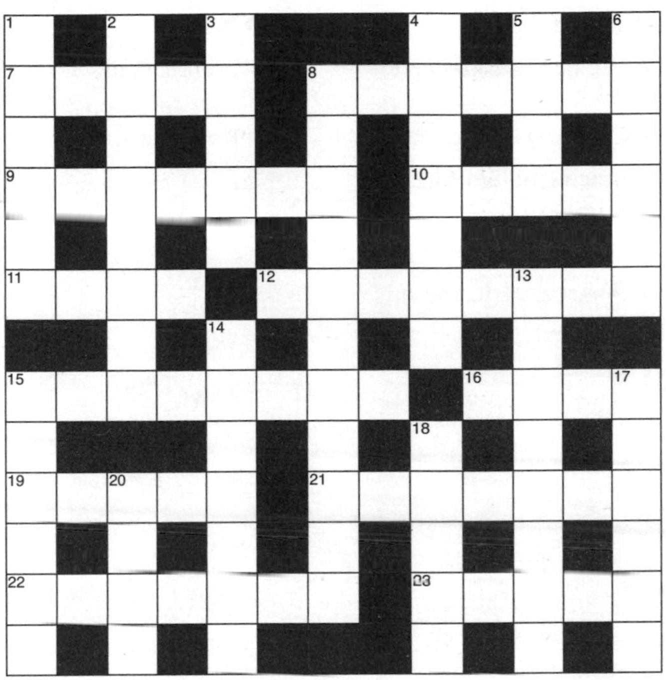

ACROSS

1 Let off (gun, prisoner) (9)

6 Crazy (3)

8 Bracing-point of lever (7)

9 Having come up (5)

10 Back (of neck) (4)

11 Dilemma (8)

13, 14 Speck in Pacific, giant carvings (6,6)

17 Scottish Sabbatarians (*informal*) (3,5)

18 Light-focusing device (4)

20 Suspicious (5)

21 Henry –, English composer (died 1695) (7)

22 Stick; staff of office (3)

23 In over-tolerant fashion (9)

DOWN

1 Self-protection (7)

2 Composed, cool-headed (4-9)

3 Fling (4)

4 Uproar (6)

5 Uncanny state (8)

6 Bad handling (13)

7 Shabby and dirty (5)

12 Treachery (8)

15 To show (7)

16 Make more intense (6)

17 Biscuit with e.g. ice-cream (5)

19 Strongly recommend (4)

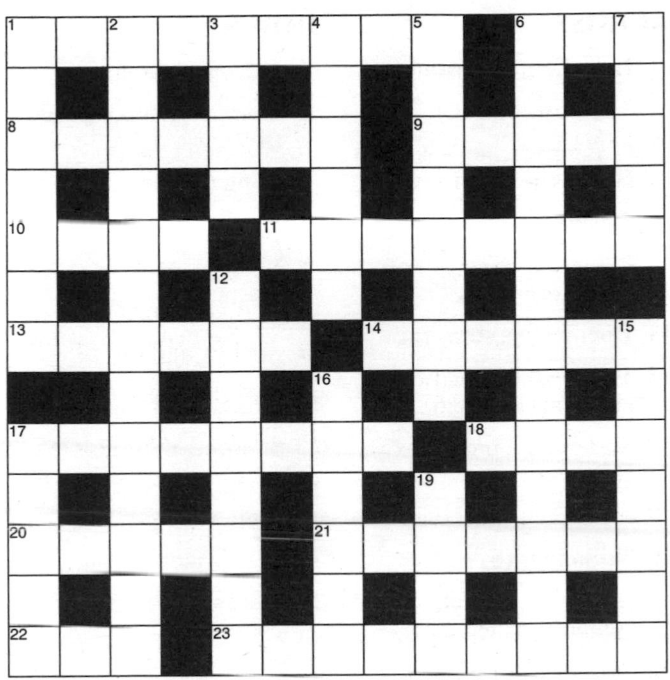

ACROSS

1 Assertion; maxim (6)

4 Self-assurance (6)

8 Glass medicine-holder (4)

9 Suicide (pilot) (8)

10 Purgation of emotions (9)

13 Track down; strap for horse (5)

15 Untrue (5)

16 Be profane; promise (5)

18 Go past (target, destination) (9)

21 Fulfilment (8)

22 Journey; stumble (4)

23 Dwell (6)

24 Obstruct; nearer the back (6)

DOWN

1 Contrivance (6)

2 Severely rebuke, punish (8)

3 Creator (5)

5 Pagan woman officiant (9)

6 By mouth (4)

7 Simple task; light wind (6)

11 Offended, insulted (9)

12 Soothing ointment (5)

14 (Vehicle) fitted with protection (8)

16 Wave-rider (6)

17 Insensible state (6)

19 Cattle-farm (US) (5)

20 Agitation (over trifles) (4)

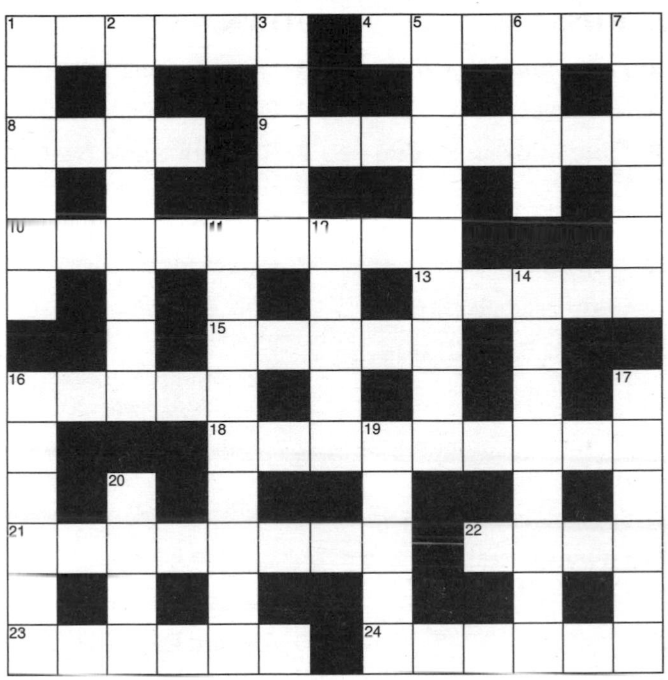

ACROSS

1 Fail to progress (3,7)

7 Viscera (7)

8 Fruit; a disappointment (5)

10 Regal rod (7)

11 Threaded fastener (5)

12 Curly salad plant (6)

15 Humble (oneself) (6)

17 Fire-raising (5)

18 Arthur's, JFK's, court (7)

21 Eagle's nest (5)

22 Scandalous event (7)

23 Five-event athletic contest (10)

DOWN

1 Wish-granting spirit (5)

2 Fortune-telling pack (5)

3 R-month-edible creature (6)

4 Bishopric of Rome (4,3)

5 Regret for wrong (7)

6 *Taming of Shrew* musical (4,2,4)

9 From time to time (3,3,4)

13 Merit, earn (7)

14 – Van Gogh (7)

16 Approach (to confront) (6)

19 Substance as e.g. gold, iron (5)

20 Acquire knowledge (5)

ACROSS

1 Laid with flags (5)

7 Anointing with oil; suave charm (7)

8 St Francis's espoused *Lady* (7)

9 City of oranges, of Barber (7)

11 Runner-up's place (6)

13 Try anyway (4,2,1,2)

15 Wrinkles by eyes (5,4)

19 Animal that gnaws (6)

21 Acrobat's garment (7)

23 Intuitive sympathy (7)

24 Portable rocket-launcher (7)

25 Girls' toys (5)

DOWN

1 Samuel –, diarist (5)

2 Briskly (*music*) (6)

3 Boldness (6)

4 Ropes; London hospital (4)

5 Rigorous (6)

6 Patchwork artform (7)

10 English city, sounds like *one leaving* (6)

12 Disagree (6)

14 A club; a weapon-store (7)

16 Moist-timber disease (3,3)

17 Sluggish, dormant (6)

18 Flinch, start back (6)

20 New Testament book; Roman emperor (5)

22 Haul; a bore (4)

ACROSS

1 Cut, shared (7)

5 Self-righteous moralist (4)

9 Map book (5)

10 Cavalryman; to coerce (7)

11 Demagogue (6-6)

12 Unclear (weather, liquid) (6)

13 Playful enjoyment (6)

16 Unemotional, plain (6-2-4)

19 Nightclub steward (7)

20 Musical drama (5)

21 Flood-containing wall (4)

22 How hope springs (*Pope*) (7)

DOWN

1 Dingy; dull brown (4)

2 Natural eruptor (7)

3 "Of Man's first –," (*Paradise Lost*) (12)

4 Midlands town; Robert –, Elizabeth I's Earl of Leicester (6)

6 Digs with snout; origins (5)

7 Not branded (drug) (7)

8 Unpaid chore (6,2,4)

12 On which to sleep in tent (4,3)

14 Bible stand (7)

15 Musical evening (6)

17 Vehicle; dealings (5)

18 Place of confinement (4)

ACROSS

7 An adhesive (4)
8 Of armorial science (8)
9 One on foot (6)
10 (Especially Cornish) fairies (6)
11 Satellite (4)
12 Nietzsche's top person (8)
15 Memento (8)
17 Sin; substitute (4)
18 Unfree persons (6)
21 Mental health (6)
22 Fabled treasure city (2,6)
23 Nipple (4)

DOWN

1 Prohibition-era gangster (2,6)
2 Indicate to approach (6)
3 Personal magnetism (8)
4 Let fall (4)
5 Magical remedy (6)
6 Rasp; dossier (4)
13 Journalists' enclosure (5,3)
14 California prison, had Birdman (8)
16 Conditioned-reflex researcher (6)
17 Conceit; pointlessness (6)
19 Wonderful thing; Berg opera (4)
20 G. B. –, *Man and 12* author (4)

ACROSS

7 Become limp; lose energy (4)

8 Chaotic; lawless (8)

9 Short, serious publication (8)

10 Without sensation (4)

11 Efficacious, forceful (6)

13 Take possession of (6)

15 Longest World War 1 battle, on Meuse (6)

17 Spotted block for game (6)

19 Cot; steal (one's ideas) (4)

21 Majestic; system of measures (8)

23 Determined (8)

24 Unwell (4)

DOWN

1 Oral exam (4,4)

2 Most important; wire fastener (6)

3 Cease to interest (4)

4 Conclusive remark; newest fashion (in) (4,4)

5 Attractive (view) (6)

6 Unyielding (4)

12 Ringing in ears (8)

14 Town of *P. Cezanne* (*anagram*) (8)

16 One owing money (6)

18 Swampy area (6)

20 Submerged ridge (4)

22 (Remove) rind (4)

ACROSS

1 Discharge of random bullet (3-4)

5 Repair (4)

9 Nervous agitation (5)

10 Solo ballet dance (3,4)

11 Laudable (12)

12 Thinly scattered (6)

13 Scurrilous (6)

16 Occasionally (4,2,1,5)

19 Pouched-bill bird (7)

20 *Gerontius* composer (5)

21 Dip (e.g. biscuit in tea) (4)

22 Meet (7)

DOWN

1 Breathe hard; light cake (4)

2 Greek restaurant (7)

3 Tendency to group together (4,8)

4 Intermittent-motion part (6)

6 Bring to bear (5)

7 Held up (7)

8 Great surprise (12)

12 Bent, lowered oneself (7)

14 Declares, makes out (7)

15 Riviera resort, has film festival (6)

17 Two-dot mark; part of body (5)

18 Nondescript colour (4)

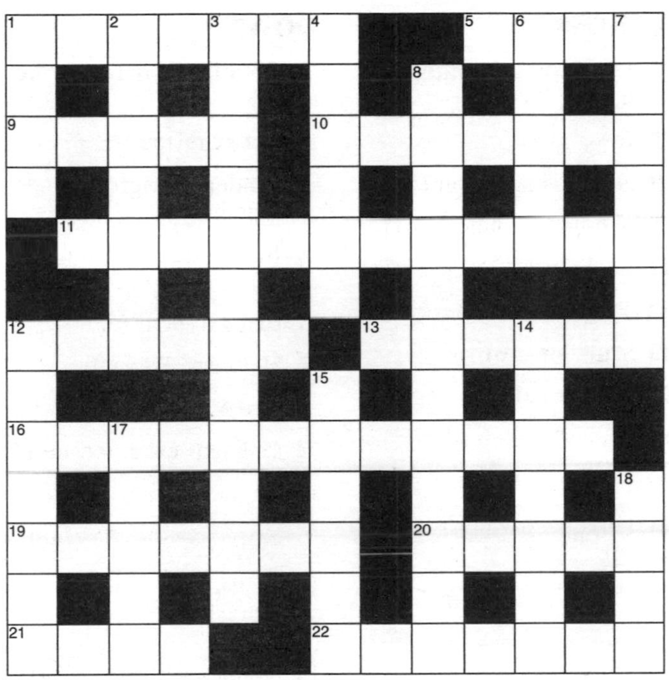

ACROSS

6 "Cotton-wool" cloud (7)

7 Equipped with weapon (5)

9 An extremist (5)

10 Whole number (7)

11 One of pack of 52 (7,4)

14 Property seller (6,5)

17 Walk awkwardly (7)

19 Puccini's opera-singer heroine (5)

21 Furnishing etc. scheme (5)

22 Rhombus; precious stone (7)

DOWN

1 Soot flake; dirty jokes (4)

2 Agreeable (8)

3 Birthplace of St Francis (6)

4 Stupid, crazy (4)

5 One leaving to settle abroad (8)

6 Weapon; association (4)

8 Tyrolean dress, skirt (6)

11 Italian poet, loved Laura (8)

12 1914-18 world conflict (5,3)

13 Skilled (in); sounds like *Russian distance* (6)

15 Item list for meeting (6)

16 (Celtic) poet (4)

18 Reveal; unadorned (4)

20 Hole for coin (4)

ACROSS

1 Seriousness; avoiding excess (8)

5 Cask-stopper (4)

9 Vegetable plot (7,6)

10 A fish; singe (4)

11 Opponent of (mechanised) progress (7)

13 Louisa May —, US author (6)

15 Subject of Genghis Khan (6)

18 Support (7)

20 Summit (4)

23 Boxing division; triviality (13)

24 Third Gospel (4)

25 Taken to task (8)

DOWN

1 Turbaned Indian (4)

2 Set of e.g. loaves (5)

3 Come into (7)

4 Complicated mess (6)

6 (One's) ruin (7)

7 Tentative (8)

8 Magician's stick (4)

12 Grail-winning knight (*Wagner*) (8)

14 Don warrior (7)

16 Tyrannise over (7)

17 Right of admission; a dish (6)

19 Dull pain (4)

21 Rage (5)

22 Collar fastener (4)

ACROSS

1 Impaled; (news story) scrapped (6)

5 Deprived (6)

8 Chess man; hock (4)

9 Arrangement within set (8)

10 Sarcastic; corrosive (7)

11 Foolish; very close (fielder) (5)

13 (Comic act) flop (3,3,5)

16 School of fish (5)

18 Religious saviour (7)

21 Spring flower; pale yellow (8)

22 Hello there (*nautical*) (4)

23 Area round Dorset (*Hardy*) (6)

24 Be characteristic of (6)

DOWN

2 Printed poster (7)

3 Chess pieces; two books of Bible (5)

4 Aerial combat (8)

5 Inky mess (4)

6 Exact copy (7)

7 Ultimate (5)

12 Supporter, hanger-on (8)

14 Old humanist; *masseur* (*anagram*) (7)

15 Prevent, intercept/divert (4,3)

17 Mob; sounds like *store* (5)

19 Overwhelm; bog (5)

20 Wheedle (4)

ACROSS

1 Parched; tedious (study) (4)

3 Ludicrous (8)

9 Desert plants (5)

10 Fishing vessel (7)

11 Current-measuring device (7)

12 Implement (4)

14 Unintelligent (6)

16 Seductive appeal (6)

18 Heel over; set of items (4)

19 Not listened to (7)

22 As 8 is of 18 (7)

23 Caribbean *voodoo* island (5)

24 Twilight (*Scottish*) (8)

25 Complacent (4)

DOWN

1 Word not in current use (8)

2 (Held) in solitary (13)

4 Blood-circulating tube (6)

5 Personal possession (7)

6 Word in informal use (13)

7 Traditional wisdom (4)

8 River sediment (4)

13 Selling (small items, drugs) (8)

15 Meantime (7)

17 Armed criminal (6)

20 Sunken boundary (2-2)

21 Group of workmen, criminals (4)

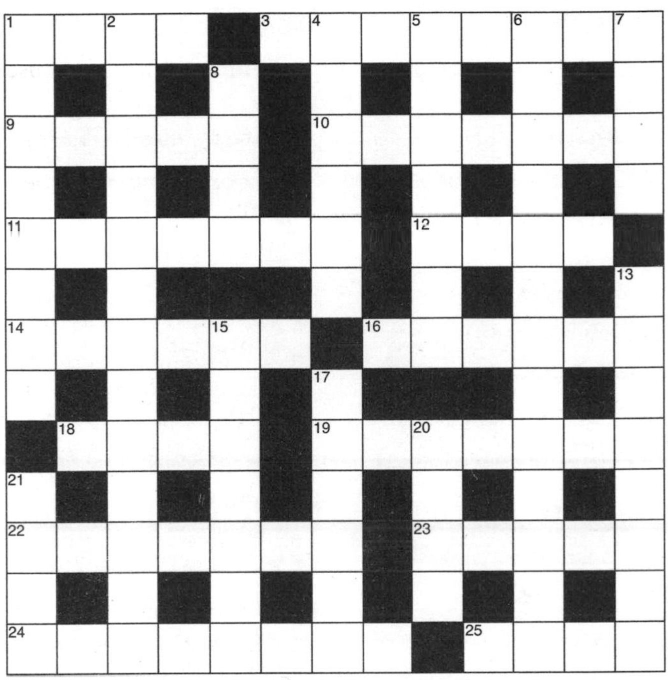

ACROSS

1 Hurl; disconcert (5)

4 Noble lady; *My Last* – (*Browning*) (7)

8 Light-blue university (9)

9 Anger (3)

10 Seize; a recording sequence (4)

11 Debilitate (8)

13 South American cloak, hole for head (6)

14 Supervisor, (e.g. college) head (6)

17 Free of charge (8)

19 Bunch of bananas (4)

22 Ordinance (3)

23 Law (9)

24 Conjugal (7)

25 Timer; observe (5)

DOWN

1 Unspoken, understood (5)

2 Savoury cheese dish (7)

3 Do a job; perform properly (4)

4 Real tennis gallery; *sanded* (*anagram*) (6)

5 Road, no stopping allowed (8)

6 – Doolittle (*Pygmalion*) (5)

7 Illicit hooch den (7)

12 Gradually cease to use (5,3)

13 Food for thought (7)

15 Pond-searching equipment; police hunt (7)

16 Of mediaeval society; of quarrel (6)

18 Shrink in fear (5)

20 "Go, and he goeth ... Do this, and he – it" (*Matt. 8*) (5)

21 Be aware of (4)

ACROSS

1 Take casual interest (in) (6)

4 Satirise (4,2)

8 Rowdy party (7)

10 Inquiry; search (5)

11 Leap; rubbish-bin (4)

12 Raider (8)

14 Abandoned baby (9)

18 Test (of e.g. actor for job) (8)

20 Cross-dressed panto role (4)

22 Energy; phase of water (5)

23 Citizen army (7)

24 Modest; coy (6)

25 Coloured pencil (6)

DOWN

1 Cease (from) (6)

2 Landowner's steward (7)

3 Simple board game (4)

5 Stress (8)

6 Edwin – (*Dickens*) (5)

7 What "gets lost in translation" (*Frost*) (6)

9 Where soldier may be under arrest (9)

13 Patron (of shop) (8)

15 Frightful; pallid (7)

16 Serried (ranks) (6)

17 Vichy Marshal (6)

19 Night-time fantasy (5)

21 Indistinct view (4)

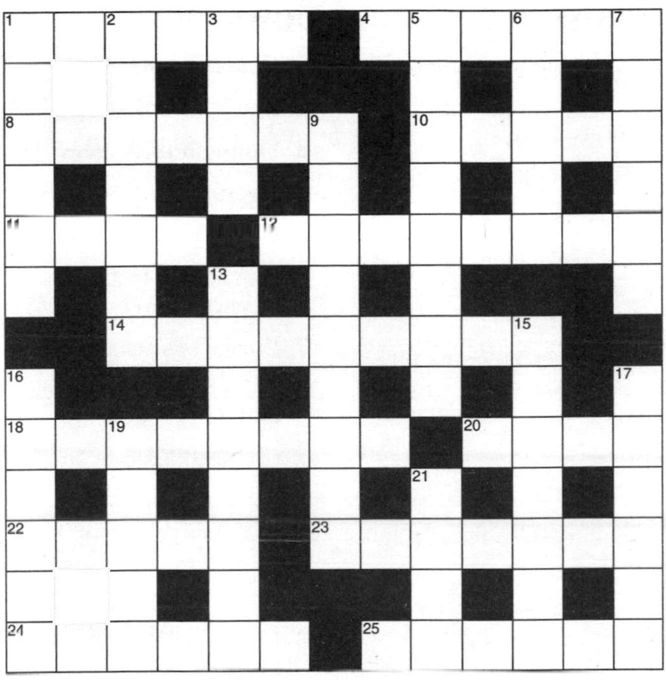

ACROSS

1 Jug; baseball-player (7)

5 Important person; ski mound (5)

8 Change (5)

9 W. E. Johns' flying hero (7)

10 We shall see eventually (4,4,4)

12 Latin verbal noun; on the back (6)

14 (Sailor) on land (6)

17 Remain imperturbable (3,4,1,4)

21 Yellowstone Park state (7)

22 Feast; children's comic (5)

23 One from Salonika (5)

24 Highest peerage rank (7)

DOWN

1 Rehearse (8)

2 Symbolic animal (5)

3 Got with difficulty (4-3)

4 Rough stone pieces (6)

5 Power (5)

6 Inquisition-victim physicist (7)

7 Luxuriant; alcoholic (4)

11 Valuable piece handed down (8)

13 Cause to happen; annoy (7)

15 South African rhino whip (7)

16 Emotionally cold (6)

18 Use brain; sort of tank (5)

19 (Give) prize (5)

20 Tiny branchlet (4)

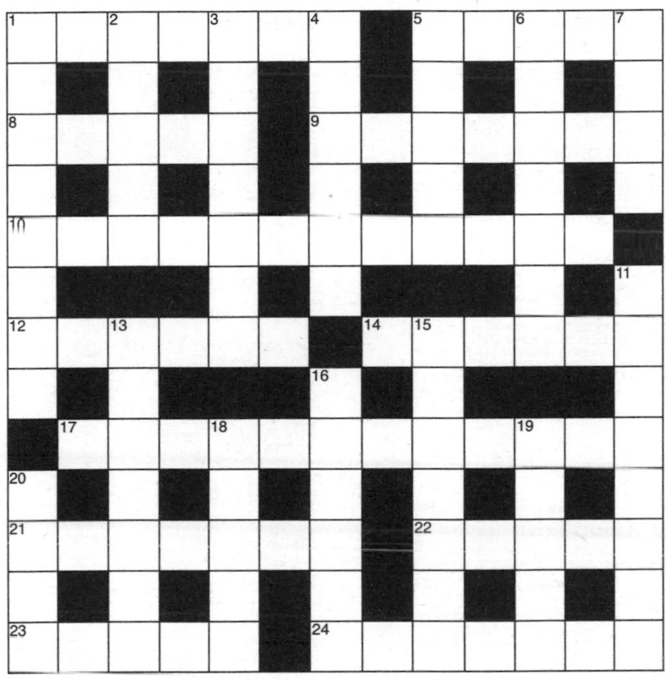

ACROSS

5 Cricket, football, side (6)

7 Incompetent (6)

9 Rebound (bullet) (8)

11 Breathe fast, shallowly (4)

12 Horse dealer (5)

13 Tell off (6)

15 French café (6)

17 (Dog) sound menacing (5)

19 Take meal (4)

20 "Nor all, that –, gold" (*Gray*) (8)

22 Of superior quality (2,4)

23 Gateman; type of ale (6)

DOWN

1 Of our new system of measures ... (6)

2 ... short distance in the old (4)

3 Acute; elusive; hard to grasp (6)

4 Dispatched (4)

6 Out of the ordinary (11)

8 German region, has *gâteau* (5,6)

10 Jean Baptiste –, landscapist (5)

14 Counterfeit (5)

16 Rue (6)

18 Non-trick-winning cards (6)

19 Caucus-race organiser (*Alice*) (4)

21 Zulu regiment (4)

ACROSS

1 Free, emotional composition (8)

5 Rebounding sound (4)

8 Raised structure; thick sole (8)

9 Upright support post (4)

11 Gangway (5)

12 Financial supporter (7)

13 Of the lips (6)

15 One that vets (6)

18 All-powerful cure (7)

19 Lowest deck (5)

21 Colleague, supporter (4)

22 Unstable (8)

23 (Plane) run along ground (4)

24 A taking apart for examination (8)

DOWN

1 Archangel; Renaissance artist (7)

2 Collect in a heap (5)

3 Toleration; tacit consent (10)

4 Compulsion (6)

6 Frame (of car) (7)

7 Remote from centre (5)

10 Show obedience (4,2,4)

14 Three original EC members (7)

16 Subjugate; banish (thoughts) (7)

17 Heavy gun; billiard stroke (6)

18 Intertwined hair (5)

20 – Pasteur, Armstrong (5)

ACROSS

1 Non-deciduous trees (10)

8 Lamentational (poem) (7)

9 Quickly prepare; incur (3,2)

10 Slender (4)

11 Spanish Jew (8)

13 Church teaching (5)

14 Arrest; treat (new car) gently (3,2)

16 Sherlock Holmes's antagonist (8)

17 Tube; wind instrument (4)

20 Of the nose (5)

21 Roman town, buried by Vesuvius (7)

22 Blowfly; policeman (*slang*) (10)

DOWN

1 Occurrence (5)

2 Formal dinner wear (7,5)

3 Stone particles; courage (4)

4 5 town; type of cake (6)

5 "I am constant as the – star" (*Julius Caesar*) (8)

6 Stubborn (12)

7 Possible choice (6)

12 Following similar course (8)

13 Require, insist on (6)

15 Treeless plain (6)

18 Banish (5)

19 Projectiles for weapons (*abbr.*) (4)

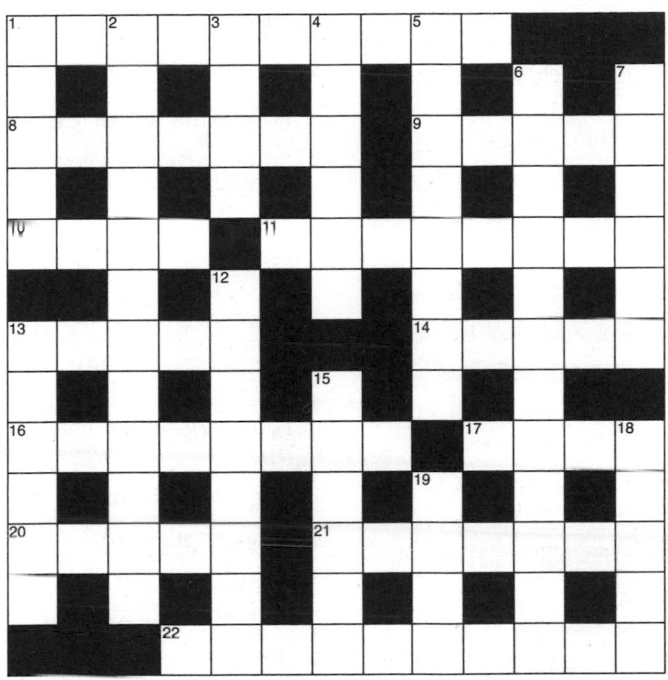

ACROSS

4 Monastic head (5)

7 What those in trouble get into (3,5)

8 Cut into cubes (4)

9 Dismiss as unimportant (5,3)

10 Disrupt (speaker) (6)

13 Container for boiling (6)

14 Importance; brief time (6)

15 Recording-room (6)

18 Give confidence; confirm (8)

19 Fizzy water (4)

20 Anglican afternoon service (8)

21 Passenger ship (5)

DOWN

1 Prosper (6)

2 Thin irregular line; run fast (6)

3 Prolonged trouble (*slang*) (6)

4 Reasoned debate; heated debate (8)

5 Obsessed (8)

6 A sweet; a nothing (6)

11 Coordinated course of action (8)

12 Sir Edwin –, animal painter (8)

14 Tidbit (6)

15 Laurence –, *Tristram Shandy* author (6)

16 Outcome (6)

17 Deep blue colour, dye (6)

ACROSS

1 Impose (the unwanted on) (5)

4 Waterfall (7)

8 Untouchable (9)

9 Lubricate (3)

10 Hair-preparation; a semi-solid (3)

11 An explosive; a Plot (9)

12 Fold, tuck (in garment) (5)

13 Touch of colour (5)

16 Get too big, old for (4,3,2)

18 Synagogue cupboard; place of shelter (3)

20 Boy child (3)

21 Lifeless (9)

22 Performer of operations (7)

23 Precise (5)

DOWN

1 Hurl; dance; love affair (5)

2 Include; implicate (7)

3 *1984* orthodoxy enforcers (*Orwell*) (7,6)

4 Chink (6)

5 Fail to conform (4,3,2,4)

6 Keep away from (5)

7 Make bigger (7)

12 Mythical winged horse (7)

14 US/Canada 4 *ac* (7)

15 Melody; exert severely (6)

17 Possessor (5)

19 Got down (e.g. to pray) (5)

ACROSS

1 Psychological battle (3,2,6)

8 W. H. –, poet (5)

9 Mass slaughter (7)

10 Crease; animal pen (4)

11 Painstaking (8)

13 Fuss; trivial objection (6)

14 Star group, may be spiral (6)

17 Odds-against competitor (8)

19 To spring (4)

22 Pungent gas, NH_3 (7)

23 Of the same value (5)

24 A vegetable casserole (11)

DOWN

1 Quay (5)

2 Danger, revolution emblem (3,4)

3 Cravenly avoid (4)

4 Greek geometer (6)

5 Perpendicular (8)

6 Quench (thirst) (5)

7 Priest's robing-room (6)

12 Single-reed instrument (8)

13 Chewy sweet (6)

15 In normal way (2,5)

16 Composer of e.g. 12 Quintet, Concerto (6)

18 Show reluctance (5)

20 Regular rhythmic beat (5)

21 Girl's admirer; dandy (4)

ACROSS

1 Put a number to (8)

5 Knock (toe); portion of ticket (4)

9 Burning (5)

10 Having bad manners (3-4)

11 Drown; succumb (2,5)

12 Sift (5)

13 Really enjoy oneself (4,1,4)

18 Improvised (2,3)

20 (Especially government) income (7)

22 Projecting fortification; defence (7)

23 Instrument; flower (5)

24 Arduous journey (4)

25 Trend; inclination (8)

DOWN

1 Unelected administrative body (6)

2 Horizontal bearing (of e.g. star) (7)

3 Heavy step (5)

4 He married Juliet (*Shakespeare*) (5,8)

6 Curt, brief (5)

7 An animal; to harass (6)

8 Largest US state (6)

14 One suffering accident, crime (6)

15 US president; shade of green (7)

16 Poor batsman; chatter (6)

17 Gift in will (6)

19 Hurry (5)

21 Strongly coloured; graphic (5)

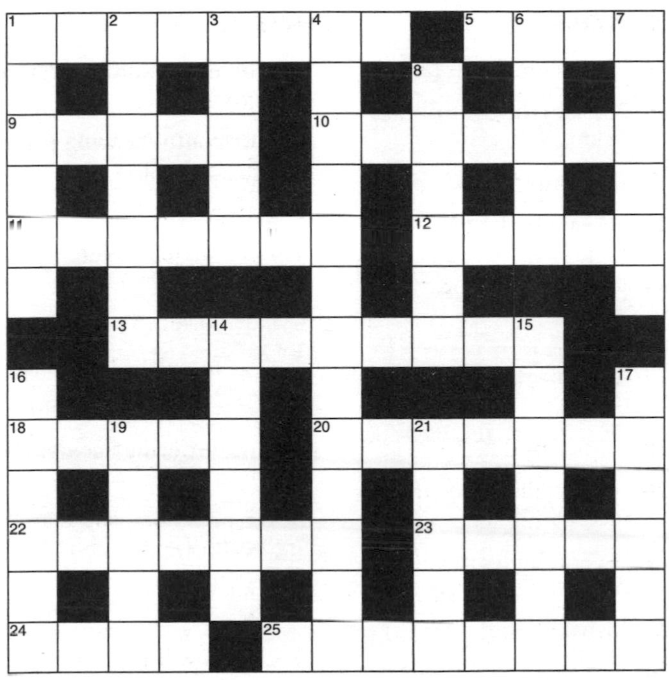

ACROSS

6 (Fight) furiously (5,3,4)

7 A sweet dish; a jolly outing (6)

8 Call into question (6)

9 Informal note (4)

10 Protruding stomach (3,5)

12 Hostile, harmful (8)

16 Flexible pipe (4)

18 Quaker; supporter (6)

20 (E.g. fin) on the back (6)

21 *Man's first disobedience* poem (8,4)

DOWN

1 Avid reader; destructive larva (8)

2 Imprison; be quiet (4,2)

3 Ceremonially oil (6)

4 Break; card game (4)

5 Gaelic hero, has Cave (6)

6 Armistice (5)

11 Outside (8)

13 Fortinbras its Prince (*Hamlet*) (6)

14 Golfer's assistant (6)

15 Climbing frame (6)

17 Shock of explosion (5)

19 Formal test (4)

ACROSS

2 Ruskin-libelled painter (8)

6 Savoury tart (6)

8 Thick, muddy (liquid) (6)

9 London cathedral (2,5)

10 South American mammal (5)

12 Weird pattern in wheat (4,6)

16 (Army) non-officers (5,5)

18 Large type of steak (1-4)

20 Easily influenced, altered (7)

21 Thundercloud; saintly aura (6)

22 Element I, its tincture an antiseptic (6)

23 Alchemical; tightly sealed (8)

DOWN

1 Breach; sever (7)

2 Very nearly (4-4)

3 Violent gust; scream (6)

4 Land to Egypt's west (5)

5 Spreading from centre (6)

7 Tournament winner (8)

11 Public money for defendants (5,3)

13 Russian (alphabet) (8)

14 Horizon; buildings seen against it (7)

15 Appalling smell (6)

17 Right to keep job (6)

19 A mollusc, the sea-ear (5)

ACROSS

1 Exchange; some false hair (6)

5 Gulp (4)

9 Swathe (7)

10 Stockholm its capital (6)

11 Emphatic, vigorous (8)

12 Landsman (*derog.*) (6)

15 Adjective modifier (6)

18 Pre-retirement performance (4,4)

20 *Way down upon* this river (*S. C. Foster*) (6)

22 Coarsely behaved (7)

23 Dominion; totter (4)

24 Flights of bees (6)

DOWN

2 Cricket annual (6)

3 Get across (8)

4 Barrier; protect risk (5)

6 Diminish (light, power) (4)

7 Mourn (6)

8 Grinding tool (6)

13 Cabbage, turnip etc. plant (8)

14 Preoccupy (6)

16 Prospects for water (6)

17 Motet (6)

19 Awry (5)

21 Exploding star (4)

ACROSS

1 Pond plant; run to attack (4)

3 Contiguous (8)

8 Soft roll (7)

10 Something to write on, to sleep on (5)

11 Its grin stayed longest (*Carroll*) (8,3)

13 Kind; science journal (6)

15 Uncivilised; fierce (6)

17 Polite, obliging (11)

20 One from outer space (5)

21 (View) that can be held (7)

22 – Swinburne; – Moncrieff (*Wilde - Importance*) (8)

23 Leave out (4)

DOWN

1 Ruddy (8)

2 Work slackly (*slang*) (5)

4 Depressingly dull (6)

5 Club; friendship (11)

6 Daughter of Agamemnon (7)

7 Ballet skirt (4)

9 *Moonlight Sonata* key (1,5,5)

12 Having perceptions (8)

14 Mattress fabric; making clock noise (7)

16 Very drunk (*slang*) (6)

18 Cuttings book (5)

19 Icelandic family story (4)

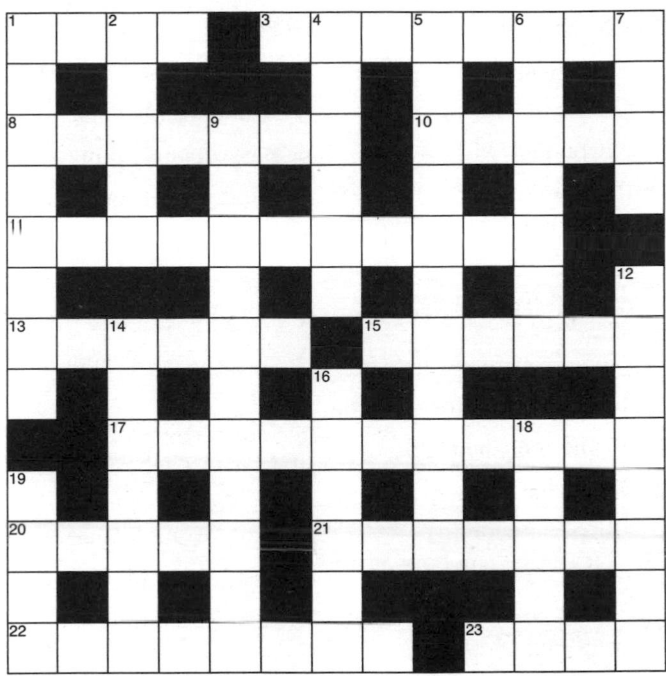

ACROSS

1 Narrow squeak (5,5)

9 Generally; a garment (7)

10 Up, on map (5)

11 Unit of molecule (4)

12 In no way; don't mention it (3,2,3)

14 Conspiracy of producers (6)

15 Brief rainfall; demonstrator? (6)

18 Of Iberian origin (8)

20 Small clue (4)

22 Go; permission (5)

23 Bird; game of dare (7)

24 (Drug) withdrawal symptoms (4,6)

DOWN

2 Accidental escape (4)

3 Not often (6)

4 Bask in natural rays (8)

5 Principal artery (5)

6 Raising the spirits (12)

7 Soft (drink) (3-9)

8 Greedily swallow (6)

13 Showing cultural decline (8)

16 Scotch (but not Irish) (6)

17 (Military) surrounding (movement) (6)

19 Little (5)

21 Contemptible, cheap (4)

ACROSS

1 Idle chat (6)

5 Male deer; try to throw rider (4)

8 Boggy ground (4)

9 Departing from norm (8)

10 Roy Plomley interviewee once (8)

11 Baghdad its capital (4)

12 One out of place (6)

14 Catalyst protein in cell (6)

16 Dressed (in) (4)

18 Unwhipped division (4,4)

20 Stéphane –, French symbolist (8)

21 Orchestra; ring (4)

22 Norse thunder god (4)

23 Wiping cloth (6)

DOWN

2 Japanese paper-folding (7)

3 Old wheat; made (a word) (5)

4 Take dangerous risks (4,4,4)

5 Hector –, French composer (7)

6 Long-line dance (5)

7 Title of Dean (4,8)

13 Violinist; type of crab (7)

15 Afternoon performance (7)

17 Dog lead (5)

19 Atmosphere, feelings (*slang abbr.*) (5)

ACROSS

1 Confirm by ticking list (5,3)

7 Cattily belittling (5)

8 Manage in unplanned way (9)

9 Record; block of wood (3)

10 Ship's base structure (4)

11 Fruit; — -ripe (*Herrick*) (6)

13 Nurse; nun (6)

14 Parchment curled up (6)

17 A 4; sounds like *gazes* (6)

18 (Clouds) move swiftly (4)

20 Vehicle; the front (3)

22 Hearten (9)

23 Gnash; wear down (5)

24 Inner and Outer Scottish islands (8)

DOWN

1 Fissure; weakness, in armour (5)

2 Put into words (7)

3 Round handle (4)

4 Air journey (6)

5 Oz kettle; may be Silly, Puffing (5)

6 Shore bird (7)

7 Stealth, concealment (7)

12 Transmitted along (7)

13 Rescue (from shipwreck) (7)

15 Field of fruit (7)

16 Obscure prophecy (6)

17 Proverbially slow creature (5)

19 Clothing; align (5)

21 German industry area, river (4)

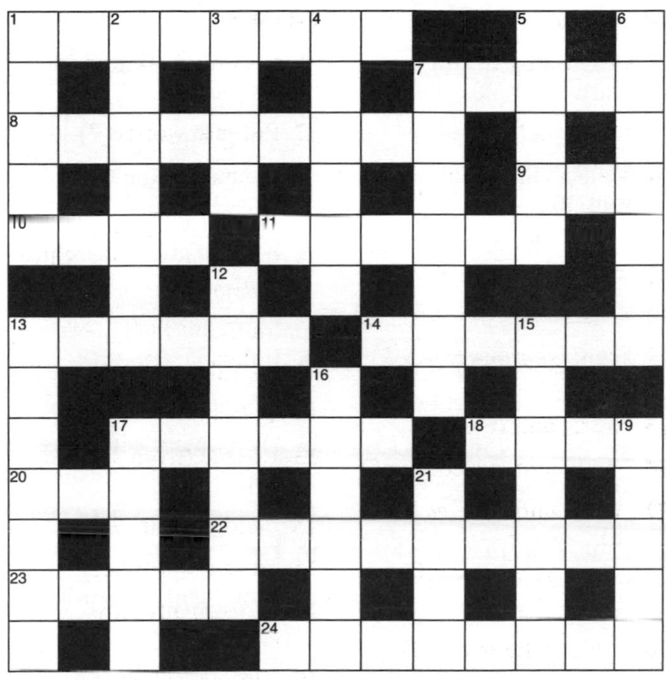

ACROSS

7 The –, Peachum/ Macheath piece (*Gay*) (7,5)

9 Minor illness (7)

10 Hard-skin fruit; has *bottle* variety (5)

11 Vigorous stylishness (4)

12 Rotation (8)

15 Taking no notice (8)

17 Fake; a pudding (4)

19 Manservant, steward (5)

21 French pilgrimage town (7)

22 –, wear it! (2,3,3,4)

DOWN

1 Give-away (4-4)

2 As best laid schemes aft gang (*Burns*) (5)

3 To some extent; attractive (6)

4 Jell; start to set (7)

5 Home of Incas, Paddington Bear (4)

6 Inflexible (rule) (4-3-4)

8 Become a nun (4,3,4)

13 Overwhelm with water (8)

14 Be nervous; a bet (7)

16 Deep bow (6)

18 Prominent up-brushed tuft (5)

20 One from Riga (4)

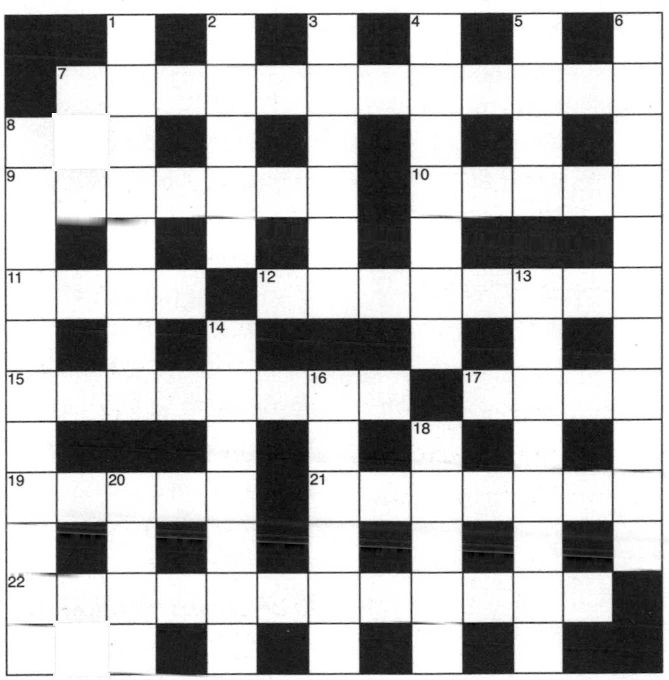

ACROSS

8 Fish exhibitions (7)

9 English county; Devereux earldom (5)

10 Murderer; a razor (9)

11 Son-in-law of the Prophet (3)

12 Involuntary, convulsive, movement (5)

14 Foot lever (7)

15 Astronomical calendar (7)

17 Trial panellist (5)

19 Trick; study (3)

20 Unwilling (9)

22 Inserted map, page; teacher training day (5)

23 Frozen block in drink (3,4)

DOWN

1 Faction; sort of race (*Alice*) (6)

2 Upset, wound (4)

3 Greek abbot; *radiance, mirth* (*anagram*) (13)

4 A seasoned stew (6)

5 Biker's accessory (7,6); fish, larva (13)

6 One from e.g. Man (8)

7 Cease to be valid (6)

13 Rebuke (8)

15 North polar region (6)

16 Town *lying in* Mary I's *heart* (6)

18 For preference (6)

21 Shivering fit (4)

ACROSS

1 Odyssey author (5)

4 Ulysses – Grant; Wallis – (7)

8 Decorations (9)

9 Tea-brewing vessel (3)

10 Consume by fire (4)

11 Have one leg either side of (8)

13 Comfort in distress (6)

14 Tough outside (as bread) (6)

17 Seaweed gelatin (4-4)

19 Soothing ointment (4)

22 First note of scale; sounds like *flour/water* (3)

23 Janitor; interim (office-holder) (9)

24 Rich (7)

25 A rustic; Dr. Johnson's cat (5)

DOWN

1 Thermonuclear weapon (1-4)

2 Uncertain-parentage dog (7)

3 Play boisterously (4)

4 Upper House (6)

5 Slaughter (8)

6 Measure (sea) depth; valid (5)

7 Convent (7)

12 Short-tempered; poor-quality (LP) (8)

13 Fame, as entertainer (7)

15 Piled neatly (7)

16 Loathing (6)

18 Very pale (shocked face) (5)

20 Verge (*poet.*); butter substitute (5)

21 Restless desire (4)

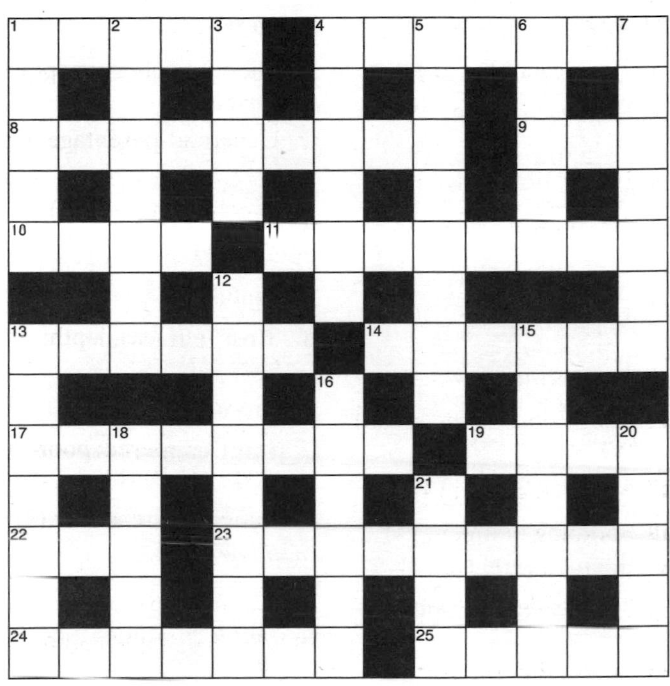

ACROSS

1 River-race festival (7)
5 Theme (5)
8 Keep firm hold of (5)
9 Well behaved; 5 *dn* (7)
10 One from the capital (8)
11 Spurn (lover) (4)
13 Police etc. entry authority (6,7)
16 Peak; horn of moon (4)
17 Asphyxiate (8)
20 Restrict, imprison (7)
21 Public, open (5)
22 Ghana capital (5)
23 Relaxation of tension (7)

DOWN

1 Punic War general; Leo star (7)
2 Particle of sand (5)
3 First-rate (3-5)
4 With all ideas exhausted (2,4,4,3)
5 Neat (4)
6 "Lost" girl (*Winter's Tale*) (7)
7 Room under church (5)
12 Erupt; escape (prison) (5,3)
14 A poison; *can rise* (*anagram*) (7)
15 Playhouse (7)
16 (Often at bedtime) drink (5)
18 Gather (odd bits) (5)
19 Travel permit (4)

ACROSS

1 French 16th century astrologer, prophet (11)

7 Stoppers; advertisements (5)

8 Not deep (7)

10 Aristocrats (8)

11 Motion-transmitting mechanism (4)

13 Physical well-being (6)

15 Praying insect (6)

17 Bundle of e.g. straw (4)

18 Plain (especially cloth) (8)

21 Beloved (7)

22 Steam bath (5)

23 Fish, shocks prey (8,3)

DOWN

1 Prevent in early stages (3,2,3,3)

2 A firework; lampoon (5)

3 Family including Dante, Christina (8)

4 Scatter, banish (6)

5 Honey wine; lea (4)

6 Conspicuous; jutting defensive line (7)

9 Despite any imperfections (5,3,3)

12 Glide behind motorboat (5-3)

14 Uncaptured (2,5)

16 Fail to remember (6)

19 One excessively modest (5)

20 Go on long walk (4)

ACROSS

1 Neat keyboarded copies (11)

8 Sordid (5)

9 Lazarus's home town (7)

10 And the rest (*Latin, abbr.*) (2,2)

11 Rural labourer (8)

13 Tree, provides mace (6)

14 Fights with lances (6)

17 Cambridge mathematician once (8)

19 A fish; a singer (4)

22 Language-learner's book (7)

23 Sound (bell); be consistent (5)

24 March girls book (*Alcott*) (6,5)

DOWN

1 A sense; a small sample (5)

2 Behave insincerely (4-3)

3 A bean, makes meat substitute (4)

4 Walter Scott novel (3,3)

5 An (alcoholic) drink (*literary*) (8)

6 Informal expressions (5)

7 Greek/Turkish island (6)

12 A pear; a citrus, gives perfume (8)

13 Post-Christian "religion" (3,3)

15 Sports ground (7)

16 Sea bird, sounds like *fuel* (6)

18 Be of use (5)

20 Surface lustre (5)

21 Barge; (US) yacht (4)

ACROSS

1 Disorientation after flight (3,3)

5 Gesturing; curving (6)

8 Tartan skirt (4)

9 "The – of America is –" (*Coolidge*) (8)

10 Lay up (for disuse) (8)

12 Underworld river (4)

13 Fanatic (6)

15 High point of heavens (6)

17 Panel game (4)

19 Refutation (8)

21 Nagging old woman (8)

23 Jacob stole his birthright (4)

24 An island; a pullover (6)

25 Asphyxiate; suppress (6)

DOWN

2 One programme of series (7)

3 Door fastener (5)

4 The Rock (9)

5 Used to be; looked (*reversed*) (3)

6 Deer meat (7)

7 Unpleasant (5)

11 Idle person (9)

14 Beggar Dives spurned; one resurrected (7)

16 Hard labour (7)

18 Tsarist edict (5)

20 Rome coin-throwing fountain (5)

22 Barren; tedious (3)

ACROSS

1 Exhibition tent; summerhouse (8)

5 Mammals; crazy (4)

9 Throw away (7)

10 Prisoner restraints; domestic appliances (5)

11 Surety for prisoner (4)

12 Not exceptional (7)

14 Catch fire (6)

16 (Supply) be exhausted (3,3)

19 Tiredness (7)

21 Grand dance (4)

24 Felled tree remains (5)

25 Sewer's finger guard (7)

26 Twisted fibres; set of e.g. pearls (4)

27 Limit, edge (8)

DOWN

1 Absorbent felt pieces; walks quietly (4)

2 Prospect, e.g. down avenue (5)

3 Publicity sheet (7)

4 Severe trial (6)

6 Dull green; a "pear" (7)

7 Has an idea; possible criminals (8)

8 Extensive (4)

13 Anti-glare light fitting (8)

15 All-suits-equal (contract) (2,5)

17 Central Italian; school of Raphael (7)

18 Type of penguin; *got one?* (*anagram*) (6)

20 Stare with mouth open (4)

22 Astrological sign, September/October (5)

23 Depend (on) (4)

ACROSS

1 Draw off lees; driven cloud (4)

3 Carvings collectively (8)

8 One from Lhasa (7)

10 Police rank (*abbr.*); jolly good (5)

11 Occurring together (11)

13 1645 Parliament victory (6)

15 Cleave (to) (6)

17 Hardly any (*colloq.*) (8,3)

20 Ladle; unrivalled news story (5)

21 Less cloudy (7)

22 Ghostlike (8)

23 Walk slowly, painfully (4)

DOWN

1 Taciturn (8)

2 Wooden house; crew room (5)

4 Lawn game (6)

5 Sleep fitfully (4,3,4)

6 One with limb removed (7)

7 Mongolian tent (4)

9 Regularly-afflicted place (7,4)

12 America (3,5)

14 Imagine, assume (7)

16 Noxious vapour (6)

18 Ornamental strip; ruff (5)

19 In its existing state (2,2)

ACROSS

1 Exhausted (4,4); useless person (8)

5 Without strength (4)

9 Out of order, ruined (5)

10 Screw up; collapse (7)

11 Word formed of initials (7)

12 (Sudden) swelling (5)

13 Unwanted scraps (9)

18 Jumped (5)

20 Cattle disease, may infect man (7)

22 Victoria Falls river (7)

23 Green snooker fabric (5)

24 Magical (Nordic) character (4)

25 Ignored (8)

DOWN

1 Decree imposed (6)

2 Clothing (*archaic*) (7)

3 Relay runners' stick (5)

4 Housing; settlement (13)

6 Drive out (5)

7 Zoo, museum, worker (6)

8 Soap-film ball; risky investment (6)

14 In better condition; gasman (6)

15 Close-pressed (ranks) (7)

16 (School, club) jacket (6)

17 Lengthen (6)

19 Capital of Jordan (5)

21 Item of furniture; list of data (5)

ACROSS

1 "'*Twas the* — ..." (5)

4 Generous (supply) (7)

8 " ... *before* —, *when* ..." (9)

9 A meal; a drink (3)

10 Way out (4)

11 Rebel aboard (8)

13 Fighting team (originally Roman) (6)

14 (Horse) in the first three (6)

17 Fellow-feeling (8)

19 Solid; tricky (4)

22 Note of debt (1,1,1)

23 Indifference (9)

24 Minotaur killer (7)

25 "... *all through the* — ..." (5)

DOWN

1 Mother-of-pearl (5)

2 Decorate (food) (7)

3 Duty (4)

4 University site (6)

5 Feasible (8)

6 Eccentric, improper (5)

7 Shadow-boxed; argued (7)

12 "... *not a* — *was stirring*, ..." (8)

13 Sophist (7)

15 French country house (7)

16 Shells (peas); oh dear! (US) (6)

18 "... *not even a* —" (*C. C. Moore*) (5)

20 Slow learner (5)

21 Egyptian looped cross (4)

ACROSS

1 South American "ostrich" (4)

4 Analysis of poetic metre (8)

8 Earn degree (8)

9 Widespread (4)

10 Ignominy (5)

11 Post from admirers (3,4)

13 Jump (on prey) (6)

15 One avoiding; Dickens's was *Artful* (6)

18 Substantial, important (7)

20 Love feast; open-mouthed (5)

23 Work for, group of, three (4)

24 Of music theatre (8)

25 Public computer link (8)

26 Hastened (4)

DOWN

2 Severe (5)

3 Insect's rear section (7)

4 Skin mark; craggy outcrop (4)

5 William IV's queen (8)

6 Blood fluid (5)

7 In illegal position (football) (7)

10 Tiny taste of liquid (3)

12 Disastrous failure, especially nuclear (8)

14 Swamp; hurry too far (7)

16 Hot, inactive period (3,4)

17 Part of fish; type of deer (3)

19 Small wood; music dictionary (5)

21 Winner's reward (5)

22 Immediately following (4)

ACROSS

6 Lady's private room (7)

7 Alternative name (5)

9 Place for books, old maids (5)

10 Multi-clawed anchor (7)

11 (Living) rurally remote (2,3,6)

14 In cahoots (4,2,5)

17 Huge (7)

19 Tradesman; Sherlock Holmes's street (5)

21 Nairobi its capital (5)

22 Harmony (7)

DOWN

1 Stratagem (4)

2 Bits thrown at happy couple (8)

3 Shoe; accent (6)

4 Maori, All-Black war-dance (4)

5 Highest point; e.g. spire on tower (8)

6 Part-statue; broken (4)

8 Send water over (6)

11 State of shame (8)

12 Instrument, has slide (8)

13 Cower; psychiatrist (*colloq.*) (6)

15 "The glory that was –" (*Poe*) (6)

16 Lattice (4)

18 Close; mean (4)

20 John –, Presbyterian founder; sounds like *raps* (4)

ACROSS

1 *Three Bears* girl (10)

8 Most important; a US election (7)

9 Doctor-repelling fruit (5)

10 Unspeaking (4)

11 Most soon (8)

13 Drink in (6)

15 Passionate enthusiasm (6)

17 Tangential (8)

18 (In) place (of) (4)

21 More advanced in years (5)

22 Lord High Everything Else (*Mikado*) (4-3)

23 Seized (goods for debt) (10)

DOWN

2 Drug; China wars over it (5)

3 Bargain; wood (4)

4 Non-expert (6)

5 Slow movers; obsequious people (8)

6 Overlord (7)

7 Transparent (3-7)

8 London terminus (10)

12 Covers, hides (8)

14 Having facial hair (7)

16 Gunman in ambush (6)

19 Inspire; permeate (5)

20 Hindu meditator (4)

ACROSS

1 Plumber's ringlet (6)

5 Little case on neck-chain (6)

8 High (meat) (4)

9 (Scottish) smallholders (8)

10 Mass-for-one's-soul chapel (7)

11 Agitate (especially milk) (5)

13 Stained, tarnished (11)

16 Kills (fly) (5)

18 Busy (2,3,2)

21 Hint; close (8)

22 Fruit; appointment (4)

23 Andy –, US pop artist (6)

24 Plural of Mr (6)

DOWN

2 Embarrassed (7)

3 He composed 104 symphonies (5)

4 Black v white disturbance (4,4)

5 Crossed-curve figure (4)

6 Baseball fielder; – in the Rye, *Salinger* (7)

7 Mistake (5)

12 Shaft of satellite light (8)

14 Too fond of drink (7)

15 Sirius (3,4)

17 Girl's name; sounds like *roam* (5)

19 Classical underworld (5)

20 Bird; train track (4)

ACROSS

1 Latin, Greek (civilisation) (9)

6 Kanga's child (*Pooh*) (3)

8 Enormous; it sank (7)

9 Cultivated soil (5)

10 Trim, peel (4)

11 Shocking; unpleasant (8)

13 Borne on breeze (6)

14 Moral philosophy (6)

17 Uphill stone-roller (Greek myth) (8)

18 Epiphany visitors (4)

20 Bring into coordinated order (5)

21 Smiled widely, nastily (7)

22 Enclosure; mate of cob (3)

23 Finally result (in) (9)

DOWN

1 A dupe; breeze on water (4-3)

2 Roughly speaking (5,1,7)

3 George –, Chopin's lover (4)

4 Bird (in wrong nest) (6)

5 Able to read and write (8)

6 Arne patriotic song (4,9)

7 Brownish-yellow earth (5)

12 Answer (8)

15 Rod holding e.g. bobbin (7)

16 Blunder (6)

17 Top of head; trophy (5)

19 Closed hand (4)

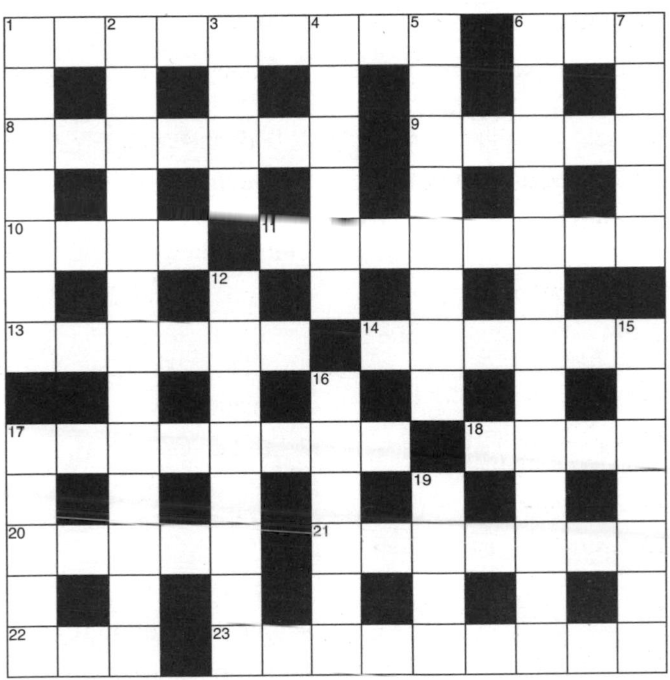

ACROSS

1 (Body) taken apart (11)

8 High-pitched alarm sound (5)

9 Mogadishu its capital (7)

10 Four legs were (*Animal Farm*) (4)

11 Flute, oboe, etc. (8)

13 (Wood) jointed; wearing 4's hat (6)

14 Tooth decay (6)

17 One-sided; resistance fighter (8)

19 Depressed; grassland (4)

22 Dishevelled (7)

23 Edible bulb; Russian dome (5)

24 In mad(ly happy) way (11)

DOWN

1 Remove trousers (as joke) (5)

2 Walk faster (4,3)

3 Catch sight of (4)

4 Diagonal-path piece (6)

5 Curative (8)

6 Indian city; sounds like *cooked meat shop* (5)

7 Doctor Who time-machine (6)

12 Mild epilepsy (5,3)

13 Clears away (spillage, last resisters) (4,2)

15 Tusks; piano keys (*slang*) (7)

16 Lose momentum (6)

18 On slope; smoothed (5)

20 French city; sailor's girl (5)

21 Performance by one person (4)

ACROSS

1 Fissure, chink (4)

3 One rejected (7)

8 In attendance; this moment (7)

9 Let in; confess (5)

10 Ladies' garment (5)

11 Lift up (7)

13 Of old age, the old (9)

17 Ribboned post, danced round (7)

19 Having tendency (to) (5)

20 Corner; old tribesman (5)

22 Shamefully secretive (7)

23 Competitor (7)

24 Strengthened seam; leather strip on shoe (4)

DOWN

1 State of rest (6)

2 With emotion (9)

3 Superficially (2,3,4,2,2)

4 Poke gentle fun at (5)

5 Purpose (3)

6 (Animal's) rope (6)

7 Improved; punter (6)

12 Hermit (9)

14 Bang; written account (6)

15 To skewer (6)

16 Throw back (6)

18 Last Greek letter (5)

21 Obtain (3)

ACROSS

1 Measure of air moisture (8)

5 Long, heroic poem (4)

9 Darling girl (*Peter Pan*) (5)

10 Singing to backing tape (pub) (7)

11 Distinguished (7)

12 Bottomless pit (5)

13 Unlike (9)

18 Projecting roof edge (5)

20 Milan opera house (2,5)

22 Speak briefly of (7)

23 Experienced, skilful (5)

24 Bonds; neckwear (4)

25 Improvident (8)

DOWN

1 Nautical cable (6)

2 People as a whole (7)

3 Sir Arthur Conan – (5)

4 Commit oneself (to risk) (4,3,6)

6 A delegated vote (5)

7 A food; very 13 from chalk (6)

8 Suave (6)

14 Relic (of long-ago animal) (6)

15 Acrobat's swinging bar (7)

16 Allow; entry document (6)

17 Aniseed aperitif (6)

19 Meeting-place (5)

21 Slap; fishing boat (5)

TIMES 2 CROSSWORD

ACROSS

1 Queer, strange (8)

5 Quit; halt (4)

9 Quake, shiver (7)

10 Quid note (5)

11 Quiz, examination (4)

12 Quips; sudden charges (7)

14 Quid pro quo (6)

16 Qualification, proviso (6)

19 Quota, share (7)

21 Quieten (4)

24 Quick (5)

25 Quisling (7)

26 Queue (4)

27 Quarter, mercy (8)

DOWN

1 Play across green (4)

2 El Greco birthplace (5)

3 Crustacean, had Quadrille (7)

4 Opposed, loth (6)

6 Of the sense of touch (7)

7 One living off another (8)

8 Prevent; stooge (4)

13 Suggestion, plan (8)

15 Act of twisting; state of being twisted (7)

17 Warm public praise (7)

18 Gradually introduce (idea) (6)

20 Tiny bit; Greek *I* (4)

22 Language of Horace (5)

23 Quarry (4)

THE SOLUTIONS

1

O	P	E	N	U	P	■	R	E	B	A	T	E
■	N	■	O	■	I	■	O	■	O	■	O	■
F	E	E	D	■	N	O	V	E	M	B	E	R
■	U	■	■	■	C	■	E	■	B	■	■	■
S	M	O	O	T	H	■	■	■	A	B	B	É
■	O	■	M	■	H	■	G	■	S	■	R	■
I	N	F	E	R	I	O	R	I	T	I	E	S
■	I	■	L	■	T	■	U	■	I	■	A	■
M	A	Z	E	■	■	■	E	S	C	U	D	O
■	■	■	T	■	P	■	S	■	■	■	L	■
S	A	N	T	I	A	G	O	■	H	A	I	L
■	C	■	E	■	U	■	M	■	O	■	N	■
V	E	S	S	E	L	■	E	S	P	I	E	D

2

S	T	O	I	C	■	C	■	■	R	■	R	■
A	■	R	■	O	■	A	C	C	U	S	E	D
C	R	I	M	S	O	N	■	■	S	■	P	■
R	■	G	■	M	■	A	S	H	T	R	A	Y
E	L	I	C	I	T	■	T		I	■	I	■
■	■	N	■	C	O	U	R	T	C	A	R	D
■	C	■	■	■	U	■	I	■	■	■	S	■
L	U	B	R	I	C	A	N	T	■	A	■	■
■	S	■	E	■	H	■	G	A	L	L	I	C
S	H	U	T	E	Y	E	■	R		B	■	O
■	I	■	O	■	■	V	E	S	T	I	G	E
C	O	U	R	A	G	E	■	U		N	■	U
■	N	■	T	■	■	N	■	S	P	O	O	R

3

N	A	R	C	I	S	S	I	■	O	S	L	O
I	■	E	■	N	■	I	■	■	■	C	■	X
G	L	A	R	E	■	L	I	F	T	O	F	F
H	■	L	■	X	■	E	■	U	■	U	■	A
T	I	M	■	C	O	N	U	N	D	R	U	M
I	■	■	■	U	■	T	■	A	■	G	■	■
E	N	L	I	S	T	■	I	N	L	E	T	S
■	■	A	■	A	■	L	■	D	■	■	■	A
W	E	L	L	B	E	I	N	G	■	T	O	M
I	■	L	■	L	■	S	■	A	■	I	■	P
D	I	A	L	E	C	T	■	M	U	R	A	L
O	■	N	■	■	■	E	■	E	■	E	■	E
W	A	S	H	■	O	N	E	S	I	D	E	D

4

■	O	P	E	N	P	R	I	S	O	N	■	■
■	■	I	■	E	■	E	■	L		E	■	H
D	I	S	B	A	N	D	■	A	L	P	H	A
E	■	T	■	P	■	S	■	P		T	■	N
B	R	E	W	■	D	E	A	D	D	U	C	K
I	■	■	■	F	■	A	■	A		N	■	Y
L	A	G	O	O	N	■	A	S	L	E	E	P
I	■	L	■	R	■	S	■	H	■	■	■	A
T	H	A	N	K	F	U	L	■	C	O	I	N
A	■	C	■	E	■	L	■	G		C	■	K
T	R	I	B	E	■	L	A	R	C	E	N	Y
E	■	E	■	P	■	E	■	I		A	■	■
■	■	R	E	S	E	N	T	M	E	N	T	■

5

L	I	O	N	C	U	B			M	A	I	M
U		R		O		U		P		D		O
L	A	D	E	N		C	O	U	P	L	E	T
L		I		D		K		T		I		T
	I	N	D	I	G	E	S	T	I	B	L	E
		A		T		T		H				S
C	E	L	T	I	C		F	E	R	M	A	T
R				O		A		B		E		
E	A	T	O	N	E	S	W	O	R	D	S	
A		I		I		H		O		I		M
S	E	M	I	N	A	L		T	I	A	R	A
E		O		G		A		I		T		R
D	O	N	E			R	A	N	G	E	R	S

6

D	A	W	N		B	E	N	J	A	M	I	N
E		I				N		O		O		O
B	I	L	K		P	E	N	C	H	A	N	T
O		D		P		R		K		N		E
N	E	W	F	A	N	G	L	E	D			
A		E		I		Y		Y		J		T
I	N	S	A	N	E		S	C	R	A	P	E
R		T		K		S		L		U		N
			S	I	N	E	Q	U	A	N	O	N
W		H		L		E		B		D		Y
I	D	E	A	L	I	S	T		M	I	S	S
S		R		E		A				C		O
P	U	B	C	R	A	W	L		L	E	A	N

7

H	O	S	T			K	E	S	T	R	E	L
U		T		S		N		A		U		A
M	O	R	O	C	C	O		T	U	B	E	R
P		A		R		W		A				D
T	I	T	L	E		W	I	N	S	O	M	E
Y		A		E		H				A		R
		G	O	D	F	A	T	H	E	R		
D		E				T		U		S		B
U	N	M	A	S	K	S		S	O	W	E	R
M				W		W		S		O		O
P	A	N	D	A		H	E	A	D	M	A	N
T		O		M		A		R		A		Z
Y	O	R	K	I	S	T			A	N	T	E

8

V	A	C	I	L	L	A	T	E		F	A	G
A		L		I		N		S		E		A
S	H	A	R	P		N	A	T	U	R	A	L
E		M				E		A		A		L
	C	O	N	V	E	X		B	E	L	I	E
		U		I		E		L				O
S	P	R	U	C	E		B	I	G	B	E	N
U				A		M		S		A		
C	O	V	E	R		U	N	H	O	L	Y	
C		I		I		S				A		F
E	N	C	L	O	S	E		Z	O	N	A	L
S		H		U		U		O		C		A
S	P	Y		S	O	M	N	O	L	E	N	T

9

P	A	S	T	I	M	E			D	U	L	L
	P		U		A		H		O		E	
R	I	B	B	O	N		A	U	G	E	A	N
	E				N		R		C		D	
S	C	A	B	B	A	R	D		O	M	E	N
	E		E				U		L		R	
		B	A	R	G	E	P	O	L	E		
	C		U		O				A		D	
V	A	S	T		B	A	L	L	R	O	O	M
	S		I		B		O				M	
F	I	T	F	U	L		D	I	S	M	A	Y
	N		U		E		G		I		I	
S	O	I	L			S	E	X	T	A	N	T

10

A	M	U	L	E	T			G	R	A	B	
	U		O		O		H		O		E	
	L	E	P	A	N	T	O		U		A	
	L		S		G		M	O	T	I	V	E
B	A	D	I	N	A	G	E				E	
	H		D				L	I	V	E	R	Y
			E		I		Y		I			
G	A	R	D	E	N				C		E	
	W				T	I	P	S	T	A	F	F
U	N	I	Q	U	E		U		U		F	
	I		U		R	A	M	P	A	G	E	
	N		I		N		P		L		T	
	G	A	T	E			S	U	S	S	E	X

11

O		F		B	A	T		T		L		E
D	R	I	V	E		R	E	A	L	I	S	T
D		N		N		A		L		T		C
S	C	E	P	T	I	C		L	A	T	H	E
		R				T		S		L		T
S	C	Y	T	H	E		W	H	E	E	Z	E
N				O				I				R
O	C	C	U	L	T		S	P	A	R	T	A
B		O		I		S				I		
B	Y	R	O	N		P	L	E	A	S	E	D
I		N		E		E		A		I		O
S	T	E	P	S	O	N		R	I	N	G	S
H		A		S		T	I	N		G		S

12

A	B	S	O	L	V	E		S	C	R	U	M
T		T		A		N		U		O		A
T	R	O	O	P		D	E	B	U	S	S	Y
E		R				U		J		E		B
M	U	M		P	I	R	O	U	E	T	T	E
P				R		E		D		T		
T	O	M	T	I	T		W	I	Z	A	R	D
		A		V		F		C				U
D	U	N	S	I	N	A	N	E		P	I	N
U		A		L		C				R		G
N	E	G	L	E	C	T		G	L	O	B	E
E		E		G		O		U		U		O
S	U	R	G	E		R	A	M	A	D	A	N

13

R	E	D	C	R	O	S	S		P	A	L	M
U		I		E		I		F		U		I
S	E	R	V	E	O	N	E	R	I	G	H	T
T		T		L		B		E		M		I
	G	Y	R	O		I	C	E	B	E	R	G
G				F		N				N		A
A	D	R	I	F	T		P	A	S	T	I	T
R		E				T		D				E
O	F	F	I	C	E	R		A	N	N	E	
T		L		H		O		P		E		M
T	H	E	D	E	V	I	L	T	O	P	A	Y
E		C		F		K		E		A		T
D	O	T	E		B	A	R	D	O	L	P	H

14

	S	M	A	T	T	E	R	I	N	G		
		I		R		L		R		U		M
S	A	S	S	O	O	N		I	N	N	E	R
T		E		D		I		S		S		S
A	I	R	Y		O	N	T	H	E	H	O	P
Y				S		O		M		O		R
A	U	B	R	E	Y		T	A	T	T	O	O
T		Y		A		E		N				U
H	I	G	H	M	A	S	S		A	M	I	D
O		O		L		T		E		A		I
M	I	N	K	E		A	T	T	A	C	H	E
E		E		S		T		N		H		
		S	Y	S	T	E	M	A	T	I	C	

15

16

17

D	E	B	I	T	■	A	R	C	A	D	I	A
I	■	U	■	R	■	L	■	O	■	A	■	L
S	T	R	A	U	S	S	■	M	O	U	N	T
A	■	N	■	S	■	A	■	P	■	N	■	O
S	T	I	N	T	■	C	R	U	F	T	S	■
T	■	S	■	■	■	E	■	T	■	■	■	R
E	X	H	O	R	T	■	J	E	J	U	N	E
R	■	■	■	E	■	S	■	■	■	T	■	L
■	N	A	U	S	E	A	■	B	R	O	K	E
F	■	L	■	E	■	C	■	E	■	P	■	A
A	M	O	U	R	■	H	I	S	N	I	B	S
I	■	F	■	V	■	E	■	O	■	A	■	E
R	E	T	R	E	A	T	■	M	I	N	E	D

18

T	R	U	N	C	A	T	E	D	■	S	E	T
W	■	N	■	U	■	W	■	E	■	L	■	H
E	N	D	O	R	S	E	■	M	I	A	M	I
L	■	E	■	T	■	N	■	O	■	P	■	R
F	I	R	E	■	S	T	A	N	D	A	R	D
T	■	S	■	M	■	Y	■	I	■	N	■	■
H	I	T	M	A	N	■	B	A	N	D	I	T
■	■	A	■	L	■	W	■	C	■	T	■	E
F	A	N	T	A	S	I	A	■	F	I	L	M
I	■	D	■	Y	■	N	■	F	■	C	■	P
F	L	I	E	S	■	T	R	I	C	K	L	E
T	■	N	■	I	■	E	■	V	■	L	■	S
H	A	G	■	A	G	R	E	E	M	E	N	T

19

20

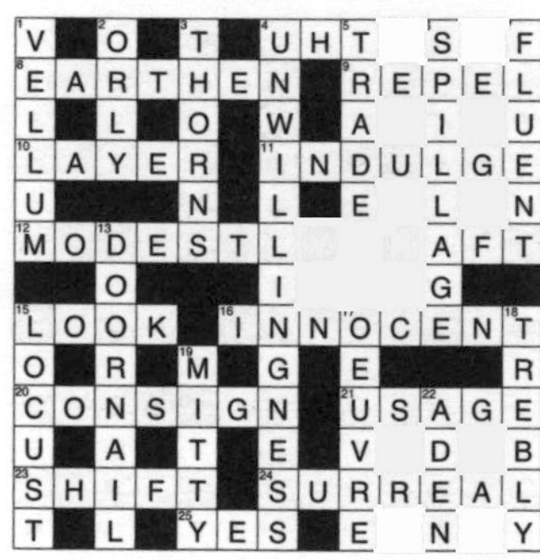

21

22

23

24

25

N	O	R	D	I	C		N	U	B	I	L	E
	B		O		O		I		U		E	
A	V	I	D		M	I	L	I	T	A	N	T
	E		G		E				C		I	
G	R	I	E	V	O	U	S		H	O	N	K
	S				F		M		E			
M	E	R	C	I	A		A	R	R	I	V	E
			R		G		R				E	
U	G	L	Y		E	N	T	I	C	I	N	G
	R		S				C		A		T	
N	O	R	T	H	S	E	A		P	L	U	M
	U		A		I		R		R		R	
S	T	O	L	E	N		D	R	I	V	E	L

26

T	E	S	T	T	U	B	E		F	I	N	D
O		A		W		U				M		A
B	A	L	L	O	O	N	S		S	P	A	R
Y		O		N		K		O		E		C
J	U	N	T	A		E	Q	U	E	R	R	Y
U				T		R		T		I		
G	A	M	B	I	T		D	O	L	L	O	P
		O		O		O		N				R
S	Y	N	O	N	Y	M		A	M	P	L	E
T		S		S		E		L		R		C
R	I	T	E		A	R	T	I	F	I	C	E
A		E				T		M		O		D
W	A	R	M		J	A	M	B	O	R	E	E

27

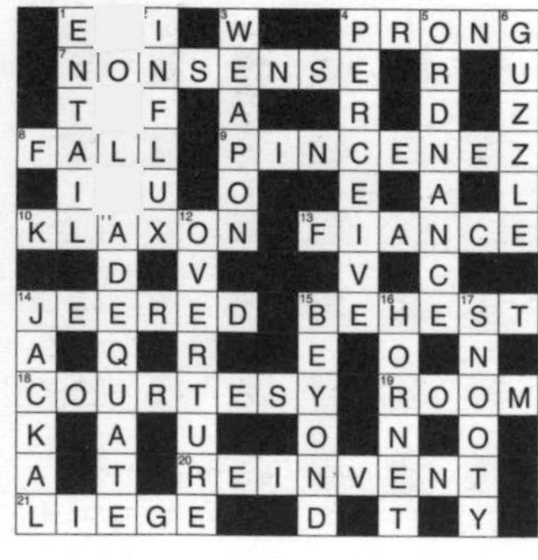

28

29

30

31

T	■	P	■	C	■	■	■	A	■	L	■	P
H	O	O	C	H	■	C	A	N	D	O	U	R
O		O		O	■	O	■	O	■	O	■	O
M	A	R	T	I	A	N	■	M	O	T	I	F
A	■	L		R	■	T	■	A	■	■	■	I
S	E	A	L	■	A	R	C	L	I	G	H	T
■	■	W		P	■	I	■	Y	■	E	■	■
D	E	S	C	R	I	B	E	■	I	N	C	A
R	■	■	■	O	■	U	■	M	■	E	■	N
O	A	S	I	S	■	T	E	A	T	R	A	Y
O		O		O	■	O	■	O	■	O	■	O
P	I	C	A	D	O	R	■	R	O	U	E	N
S		K		Y	■	■	■	I	■	S	■	E

32

33

34

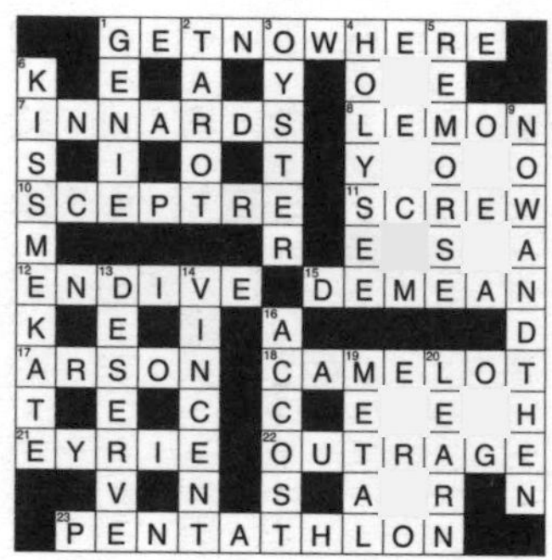

35

36

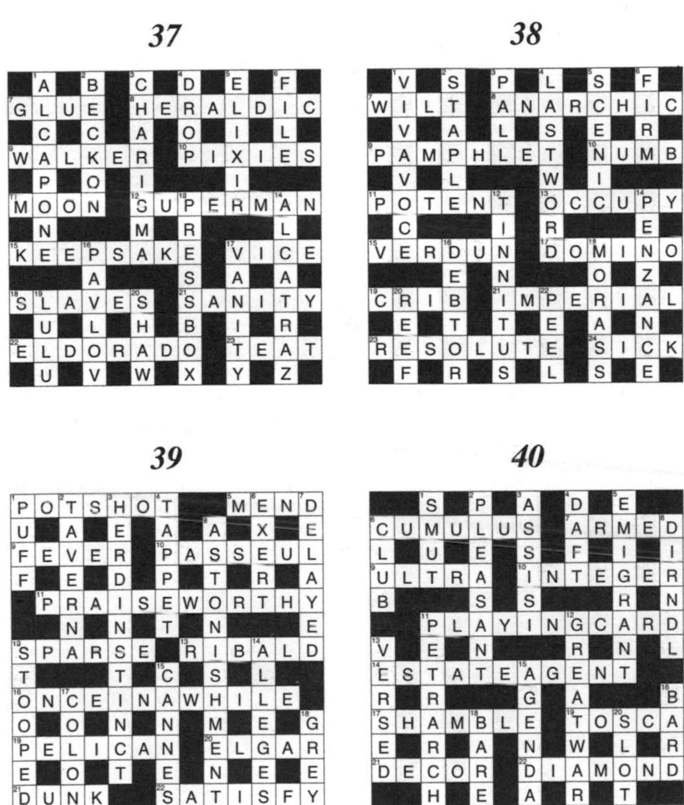

41

42

S	P	I	K	E	D		B	E	R	E	F	T
	L		I		O		L		E		I	
P	A	W	N		G	R	O	U	P	I	N	G
	C		G		F		T		L		A	
C	A	U	S	T	I	C		S	I	L	L	Y
	R				G		A		C			
	D	I	E	T	H	E	D	E	A	T	H	
			R		T		H				E	
S	H	O	A	L		M	E	S	S	I	A	H
	O		S		C		R		W		D	
P	R	I	M	R	O	S	E		A	H	O	Y
	D		U		A		N		M		F	
W	E	S	S	E	X		T	Y	P	I	F	Y

43

44

45

DABBLE SENDUP
E A U M R O
SHINDIG PROBE
I L O U H O T
SKIP MARAUDER
T F U R S Y
FOUNDLING
M S R S H P
AUDITION DAME
S R O O B S T
STEAM MILITIA
E A E U L I
DEMURE CRAYON

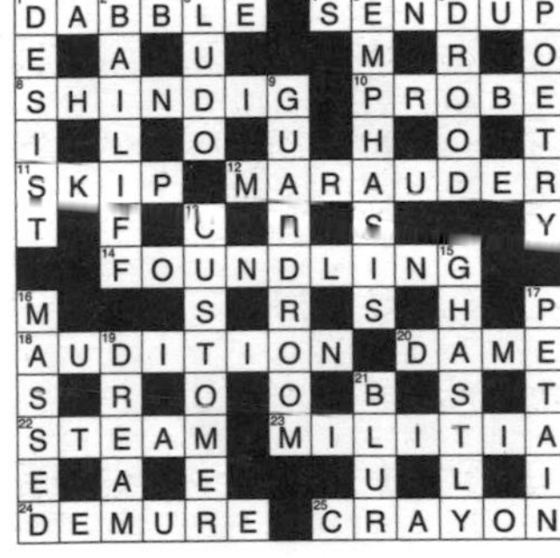

46

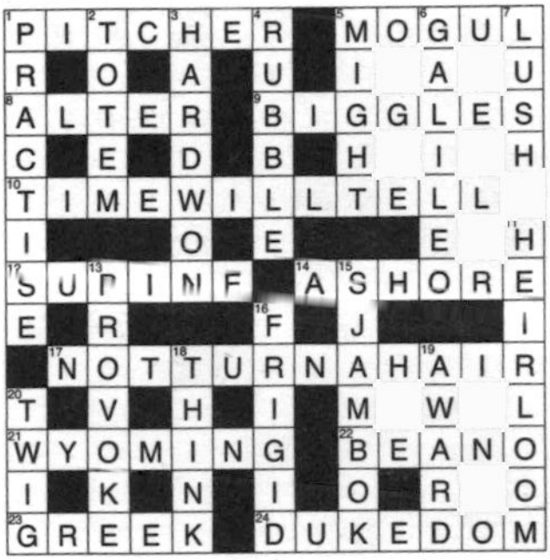
PITCHER MOGUL
R O A U I A U
ALTER BIGGLES
C E D B H I H
TIMEWILLTELL
I O E E H
SUPINE ASHORE
E R F J I
NOTTURNAHAIR
T V H I M W L
WYOMING BEANO
I K N I O R O
GREEK DUKEDOM

47

M I S S
ELEVEN UNABLE
T X C B L N
RICOCHET PANT
I E O L C
COPER REBUKE
T O O F
BISTRO GROWL
O E U R O
DINE GLISTERS
O A R M S E
DELUXE PORTER
O T I S

48

RHAPSODY ECHO
A M U U H U
PLATFORM MAST
H S F E C S E
AISLE SPONSOR
E R S M I
LABIAL CENSOR
E N C T E
PANACEA ORLOP
L E E N H O R
ALLY INSECURE
I U O E I S
TAXI ANALYSIS

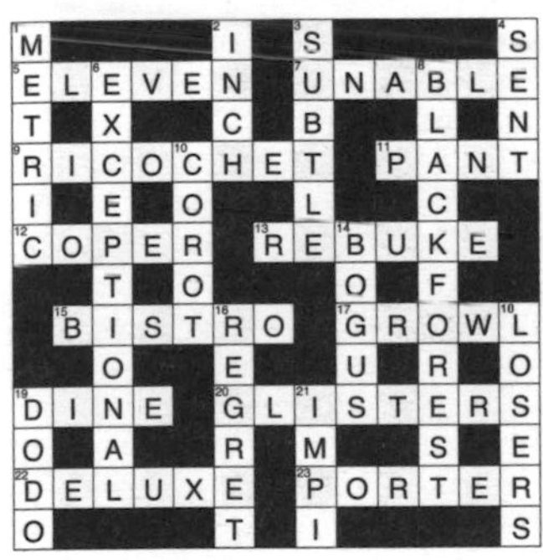

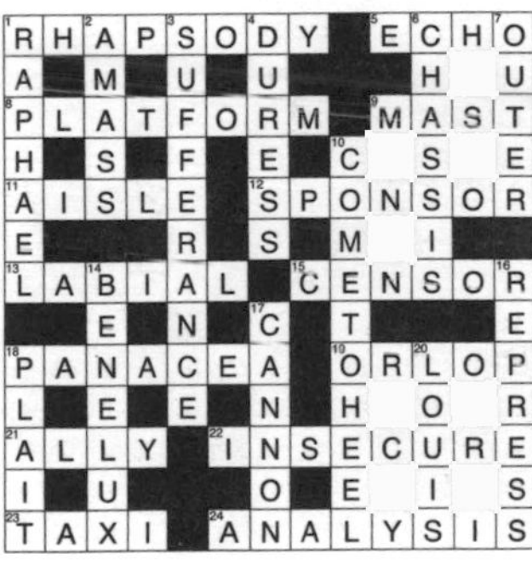

49

E	V	E	R	G	R	E	E	N	S			
V		V		R		C		O		I		O
E	L	E	G	I	A	C		R	U	N	U	P
N		N		T		L		T		T		T
T	H	I	N		S	E	P	H	A	R	D	I
		N		P		S		E		A		O
D	O	G	M	A				R	U	N	I	N
E		D		R		S		N		S		
M	O	R	I	A	R	T	Y		P	I	P	E
A		E		L		E		A		G		X
N	A	S	A	L		P	O	M	P	E	I	I
D		S		E		P		M		N		L
			B	L	U	E	B	O	T	T	L	E

50

	T		S		H			A	B	B	O	T
	H	O	T	W	A	T	E	R		E		R
	R		R		S			G		S		I
D	I	C	E		S	H	R	U	G	O	F	F
	V		A		L			M		T		L
H	E	C	K	L	E		K	E	T	T	L	E
		A		A				N		E		
M	O	M	E	N	T		S	T	U	D	I	O
O		P		D			T		P		N	
R	E	A	S	S	U	R	E		S	O	D	A
S		I		E			R		H		I	
E		G		E	V	E	N	S	O	N	G	
L	I	N	E	R			E		T		O	

51

F	O	I	S	T		C	A	S	C	A	D	E
L		N		H		R		T		V		N
I	N	V	I	O	L	A	T	E		O	I	L
N		O		U		N		P		I		A
G	E	L		G	U	N	P	O	W	D	E	R
		V		H		Y		U				G
P	L	E	A	T				T	I	N	G	E
E				P		S		O		I		
G	R	O	W	O	U	T	O	F		A	R	K
A		W		L		R		L		G		N
S	O	N		I	N	A	N	I	M	A	T	E
U		E		C		I		N		R		L
S	U	R	G	E	O	N		E	X	A	C	T

52

W	A	R	O	F	N	E	R	V	E	S		
H		E		U		U		E		L		V
A	U	D	E	N		C	A	R	N	A	G	E
R		F		K		L		T		K		S
F	O	L	D		D	I	L	I	G	E	N	T
		A		C		D		C				R
N	I	G	G	L	E		G	A	L	A	X	Y
O				A		M		L		S		
U	N	D	E	R	D	O	G		J	U	M	P
G		E		I		Z		B		S		U
A	M	M	O	N	I	A		E	Q	U	A	L
T		U		E		R		A		A		S
		R	A	T	A	T	O	U	I	L	L	E

53

Q	U	A	N	T	I	F	Y		S	T	U	B
U		Z		R		R		A		E		A
A	F	I	R	E		I	L	L	B	R	E	D
N		M		A		A		A		S		G
G	O	U	N	D	E	R		S	I	E	V	E
O		T				L		K				R
		H	A	V	E	A	B	A	L	L		
R				I		U				I		L
A	D	H	O	C		R	E	V	E	N	U	E
B		A		T		E		I		C		G
B	A	S	T	I	O	N		V	I	O	L	A
I		T		M		C		I		L		C
T	R	E	K		T	E	N	D	E	N	C	Y

54

			B		S		A		S		F	
	T	O	O	T	H	A	N	D	N	A	I	L
	R		O		U		O		A		N	
J	U	N	K	E	T		I	M	P	U	G	N
	C		W		U		N				A	
M	E	M	O		P	O	T	B	E	L	L	Y
			R						X			
I	N	I	M	I	C	A	L		T	U	B	E
	O				A		A		E		L	
F	R	I	E	N	D		D	O	R	S	A	L
	W		X		D		D		I		S	
P	A	R	A	D	I	S	E	L	O	S	T	
	Y		M		E		R		R			

55

	R				W	H	I	S	T	L	E	R
Q	U	I	C	H	E			Q		I		A
	P		H		L		T	U	R	B	I	D
S	T	P	A	U	L	S		A		Y		I
	U		M		N			L	L	A	M	A
C	R	O	P	C	I	R	C	L	E			L
	E		I		G		Y		G		S	
S			O	T	H	E	R	R	A	N	K	S
T	B	O	N	E			I		L		Y	
E		R		N		P	L	I	A	B	L	E
N	I	M	B	U	S		L		I		I	
C		E		R			I	O	D	I	N	E
H	E	R	M	E	T	I	C				E	

56

S	W	I	T	C	H			S	W	I	G	
	I		R		E		P		A		R	
	S	W	A	D	D	L	E		N		I	
	D		V		G		S	W	E	D	E	N
V	E	H	E	M	E	N	T				V	
	N		R				L	U	B	B	E	R
			S		O		E		R			
A	D	V	E	R	B				A		A	
	O				S	W	A	N	S	O	N	G
S	W	A	N	E	E		M		S		T	
	S		O		S	W	I	N	I	S	H	
	E		V		S		S		C		E	
	S	W	A	Y			S	W	A	R	M	S

57

R	U	S	H		A	D	J	A	C	E	N	T
U		K				R		S		L		U
B	R	I	O	C	H	E		S	H	E	E	T
I		V		S		A		O		C		U
C	H	E	S	H	I	R	E	C	A	T		
U				A		Y		I		R		S
N	A	T	U	R	E		S	A	V	A	G	E
D		I		P		B		T				N
		C	O	M	P	L	A	I	S	A	N	T
S		K		I		O		O		L		I
A	L	I	E	N		T	E	N	A	B	L	E
G		N		O		T				U		N
A	L	G	E	R	N	O	N		O	M	I	T

58

			C	L	O	S	E	S	H	A	V	E
N		D		E		E		U		O		X
O	V	E	R	A	L	L		N	O	R	T	H
N		V		K		D		B		T		I
A	T	O	M		N	O	T	A	T	A	L	L
L		U		D		M		T				A
C	A	R	T	E	L		S	H	O	W	E	R
O				C		P		E		H		A
H	I	S	P	A	N	I	C		H	I	N	T
O		M		D		N		V		S		I
L	E	A	V	E		C	H	I	C	K	E	N
I		L		N		E		L		Y		G
C	O	L	D	T	U	R	K	E	Y			

59

G	O	S	S	I	P				B	U	C	K
	R		P		L		V		E		O	
M	I	R	E		A	B	E	R	R	A	N	T
	G		L		Y		R		L		G	
C	A	S	T	A	W	A	Y		I	R	A	Q
	M				I		R		O			
M	I	S	F	I	T		E	N	Z	Y	M	E
			I		H		V				A	
C	L	A	D		F	R	E	E	V	O	T	E
	E		D		I		R		I		I	
M	A	L	L	A	R	M	E		B	A	N	D
	S		E		E		N		E		E	
T	H	O	R				D	U	S	T	E	R

60

C	H	E	C	K	O	F	F			B		S
H		X		N		L		S	N	I	D	E
I	M	P	R	O	V	I	S	E		L		A
N		R		B		G		C		L	O	G
K	E	E	L		C	H	E	R	R	Y		U
		S		R		T		E				L
S	I	S	T	E	R		S	C	R	O	L	L
A				L		O		Y		R		
L		S	T	A	I	R	S		S	C	U	D
V	A	N		Y		A		R		H		R
A		A		E	N	C	O	U	R	A	G	E
G	R	I	N	D		L		H		R		S
E		L			H	E	B	R	I	D	E	S

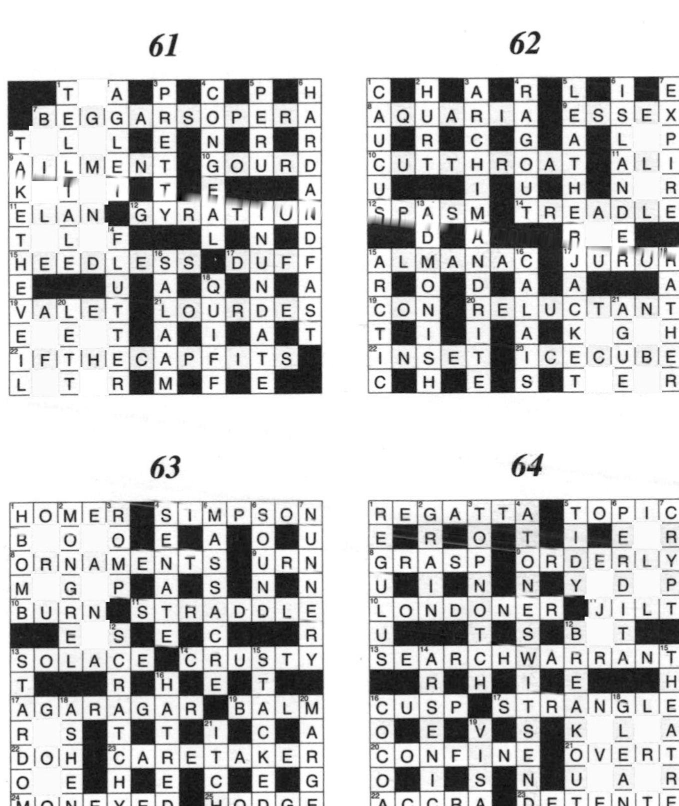
61
62
63
64

65

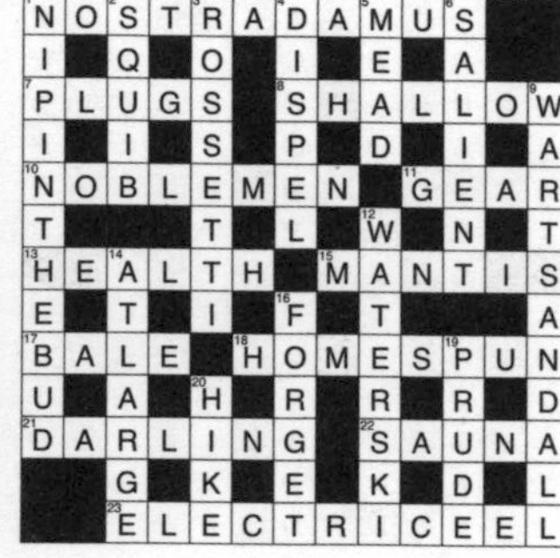

66

67

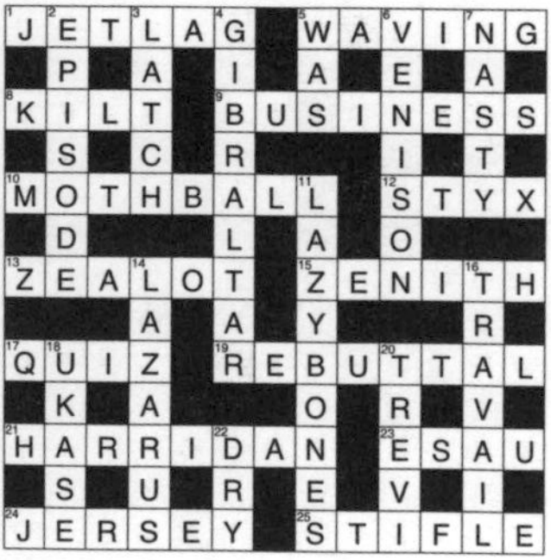

J	E	T	L	A	G		W	A	V	I	N	G
	P		A		I		A		E		A	
K	I	L	T		B	U	S	I	N	E	S	S
	S		C		R				I		T	
M	O	T	H	B	A	L	L		S	T	Y	X
	D				L		A		O			
Z	E	A	L	O	T		Z	E	N	I	T	H
			A		A		Y				R	
Q	U	I	Z		R	E	B	U	T	T	A	L
	K		A				O		R		V	
H	A	R	R	I	D	A	N		E	S	A	U
	S		U		R		E		V		I	
J	E	R	S	E	Y		S	T	I	F	L	E

68

69

70

71

N	I	G	H	T		C	O	P	I	O	U	S
A		A		A		A		O		U		P
C	H	R	I	S	T	M	A	S		T	E	A
R		N		K		P		S		R		R
E	X	I	T		M	U	T	I	N	E	E	R
		S		C		S		B				E
C	O	H	O	R	T		P	L	A	C	E	D
A				E		S		E		H		
S	Y	M	P	A	T	H	Y		H	A	R	D
U		O		T		U		A		T		U
I	O	U		U	N	C	O	N	C	E	R	N
S		S		R		K		K		A		C
T	H	E	S	E	U	S		H	O	U	S	E

72

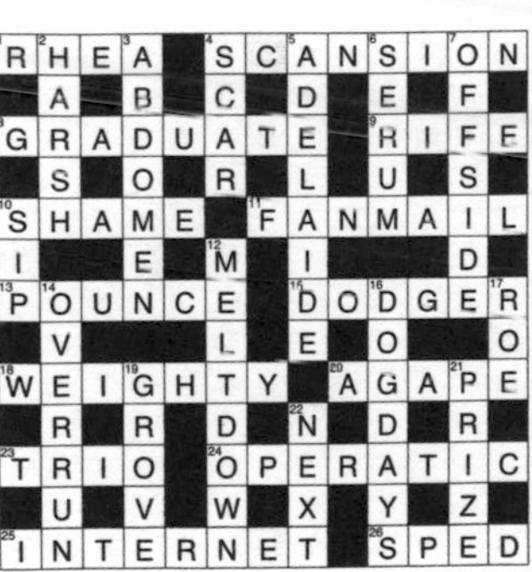

73

■	■	R	■	C	■	B	■	H	■	P	■	■
B	O	U	D	O	I	R	■	A	L	I	A	S
U	■	S	■	N	■	O	■	K	■	N	■	P
S	H	E	L	F	■	G	R	A	P	N	E	L
T	■	■	■	E	■	U	■	■	■	A	■	A
■	■	I	N	T	H	E	S	T	I	C	K	S
S	■	G	■	T	■	■	■	R	■	L	■	H
H	A	N	D	I	N	G	L	O	V	E	■	■
R	■	O	■	■	■	R	■	M	■	■	■	G
I	M	M	E	N	S	E	■	B	A	K	E	R
N	■	I	■	E	■	E	■	O	■	N	■	I
K	E	N	Y	A	■	C	O	N	C	O	R	D
■	■	Y	■	R	■	E	■	E	■	X	■	■

74

■	G	O	L	D	I	L	O	C	K	S	■	■
■	■	P	■	E	■	A	■	R		U	■	S
P	R	I	M	A	R	Y	■	A	P	P	L	E
A	■	U	■	L	■	M	■	W		R		E
D	U	M	B	■	E	A	R	L	I	E	S	T
D	■	■	■	O	■	N	■	E		M		H
I	M	B	I	B	E	■	A	R	D	O	U	R
N	■	E	■	S	■	S	■	S	■	■	■	O
G	L	A	N	C	I	N	G	■	L	I	E	U
T	■	R	■	U	■	I	■	Y		M		G
O	L	D	E	R	■	P	O	O	H	B	A	H
N	■	E	■	E	■	E	■	G		U	■	■
■	■	D	I	S	T	R	A	I	N	E	D	■

75

W	A	S	H	E	R	■	L	O	C	K	E	T
■	B	■	A	■	A	■	O	■	A	■	R	■
G	A	M	Y	■	C	R	O	F	T	E	R	S
■	S	■	D	■	E	■	P	■	C	■	O	■
C	H	A	N	T	R	Y	■	C	H	U	R	N
■	E	■	■	■	I	■	M	■	E	■	■	■
■	D	I	S	C	O	L	O	U	R	E	D	■
■	■	■	O	■	T	■	O	■	■	■	O	■
S	W	A	T	S	■	O	N	T	H	E	G	O
■	A	■	T	■	R	■	B	■	A	■	S	■
I	N	T	I	M	A	T	E	■	D	A	T	E
■	D	■	S	■	I	■	A	■	E	■	A	■
W	A	R	H	O	L	■	M	E	S	S	R	S

76

C	L	A	S	S	I	C	A	L	■	R	O	O
A	■	F	■	A	■	U	■	I	■	U		C
T	I	T	A	N	I	C	■	T	I	L	T	H
S	■	E	■	D	■	K	■	E		E		R
P	A	R	E	■	H	O	R	R	I	B	L	E
A	■	A	■	R	■	O	■	A		R	■	■
W	A	F	T	E	D	■	E	T	H	I	C	S
■	■	A	■	S	■	B	■	E		T		P
S	I	S	Y	P	H	U	S	■	M	A	G	I
C	■	H	■	O	■	N	■	F		N		N
A	L	I	G	N	■	G	R	I	N	N	E	D
L	■	O	■	S	■	L	■	S		I		L
P	E	N	■	E	V	E	N	T	U	A	T	E

77

D	I	S	M	E	M	B	E	R	E	D	■	■
E		T		S	■	I	■	E	■	E	■	T
B	L	E	E	P	■	S	O	M	A	L	I	A
A		P		Y	■	H	■	E	■	H	■	R
G	O	O	D	■	W	O	O	D	W	I	N	D
■	■	U		P	■	P	■	I	■	■	■	I
M	I	T	R	E	D	■	C	A	R	I	E	S
O	■	■	■	T	■	F	■	L	■	V	■	■
P	A	R	T	I	S	A	N	■	D	O	W	N
S		A		T	■	L	■	S	■	R	■	A
U	N	K	E	M	P	T	■	O	N	I	O	N
P	■	E		A	■	E	■	L	■	E	■	C
■	■	D	E	L	I	R	I	O	U	S	L	Y

78

R	I	F	T	■	■	O	U	T	C	A	S	T
E	■	E	■	B	■	N	■	E		I		E
P	R	E	S	E	N	T	■	A	D	M	I	T
O	■	L	■	T	■	H	■	S	■	■	■	H
S	K	I	R	T	■	E	L	E	V	A	T	E
E	■	N	■	E	■	F	■	■	■	N	■	R
■	■	G	E	R	I	A	T	R	I	C	■	■
I	■	L	■	■	■	C	■	E		H	■	R
M	A	Y	P	O	L	E	■	P	R	O	N	E
P	■	■	■	M	■	O	■	O		R		J
A	N	G	L	E	■	F	U	R	T	I	V	E
L	■	E	■	G	■	I	■	T		T		C
E	N	T	R	A	N	T	■	■	W	E	L	T

79

H	U	M	I	D	I	T	Y	■	E	P	I	C
A		A	■	O	■	A	■	U	■	R	■	H
W	E	N	D	Y	■	K	A	R	A	O	K	E
S		K		L	■	E	■	B	■	X	■	E
E	M	I	N	E	N	T	■	A	B	Y	S	S
R	■	N	■	■	■	H	■	N	■	■	■	E
■	■	D	I	F	F	E	R	E	N	T	■	■
P	■	■	■	O	■	P	■	■	■	R	■	P
E	A	V	E	S	■	L	A	S	C	A	L	A
R		E		S	■	U	■	M	■	P	■	S
M	E	N	T	I	O	N	■	A	D	E	P	T
I		U		L	■	G	■	C	■	Z	■	I
T	I	E	S	■	F	E	C	K	L	E	S	S

80

P	E	C	U	L	I	A	R	■	S	T	O	P
U	■	R	■	O	■	V	■	F		A		A
T	R	E	M	B	L	E	■	O	N	C	E	R
T	■	T	■	S	■	R	■	I	■	T		A
■	T	E	S	T	■	S	A	L	L	I	E	S
P	■	■	■	E	■	E	■	■	■	L		I
R	E	T	U	R	N	■	C	A	V	E	A	T
O	■	O	■	■	■	I	■	C	■	■	■	D
P	O	R	T	I	O	N	■	C	A	L	M	■
O	■	S	■	O	■	S	■	L		A		P
S	W	I	F	T	■	T	R	A	I	T	O	R
A	■	O	■	A	■	I	■	I		I		E
L	I	N	E	■	C	L	E	M	E	N	C	Y

NOTES

NOTES

NOTES